ECOCIDE AND POPULUTION

PERSPECTIVES

Ecocide and Popolution

MICHAEL E. ADELSTEIN AND JEAN G. PIVAL, EDITORS
University of Kentucky

ST. MARTIN'S PRESS
New York

AFFILIATED PUBLISHERS: Macmillan and Company, Limited, London—also at
Bombay, Calcutta, Madras, and Melbourne; The Macmillan Company of Canada,
Limited, Toronto.

Preface

Ecocide and Population is the first book in the Perspectives Series—collections of essays that offer insight into significant issues confronting humanity today. The books in this series will not make the reader an expert on the issues they discuss; they are designed instead to make him aware of various aspects of contemporary problems, to raise questions about and to open for discussion topics that are too complex to be fully explored in a single volume.

For *Ecocide and Population* we have selected essays on population growth and environmental decay, problems that many experts see as necessarily related. These essays, which are provocative and controversial, are arranged so that at least two views on each topic are presented.

The first section, PROBLEM, begins with William Bowen's extended definition of ecology, "Our New Awareness of the Great Web." "The Historical Roots of Our Ecologic Crisis" by Lynn White, Jr., places the blame for our current environmental problems on the Judeo-Christian philosophical tradition. In "Control of Population" Robert Ardrey argues, on the other hand, that the problem of overpopulation stems from man's evolutionary loss of the ability to exploit the population controls provided by nature.

In CONTROVERSY, the essays are subdivided by topic: Population, Pesticides, and Progress. *Population* is made up of two essays that plead the urgency of immediate population control: Paul Ehrlich's "Eco-Catastrophe" and Wayne H. Davis's "Overpopulated America." A third essay, Ben Wattenberg's "Overpopulation As a Crisis Issue: The Nonsense Explosion," attacks their general position as overstated and misleading.

The first essay in *Pesticides*, "Nature Fights Back," is a chapter from Rachel Carson's *Silent Spring*, which many consider the catalyst for the present concern about ecology. It argues that our indiscriminate use of DDT and other pesticides has resulted in the destruction of natural insect controls and the creation of new insect plagues. James W. Wright's "DDT: It Is Needed Against Malaria, but for the Whole Environment . . ." makes a strong case for the beneficial contribution of DDT and its continued use.

In *Progress*, John Neary's "Hello Energy. Good-bye Big Sky" deplores industrial destruction of an area having great natural beauty. James Michener's "Preserving Our Environment" reluctantly allows that some wild places must be sacrificed to people but urges that we attempt to conserve the beauty of nature even as we employ it to our own ends.

In the final section, SOLUTION, all authors agree that man must search for a solution to the ecological crisis, but each offers a different approach. In "Think Little" Wendell Berry advocates individual responsibility, while Victor Cohn's "But Who Will Pay the Piper and Will It Be in Time?" outlines specific types of political and social action concerned citizens might take. In "Introduction to *Ecotactics*," Ralph Nader urges that groups of individuals, in particular students, become actively involved in exposing the governmental and corporate structures that contribute to and legitimize what he calls "environmental violence."

RECOMMENDED READINGS, on page 119, is a selected bibliography of books for further study, many of which have already become classics in the field.

We hope that the variety of opinions expressed in *Ecocide and Population* will encourage the reader to explore further the issues discussed here and to reach his own conclusions about what might, or must, be done.

Michael E. Adelstein
Jean G. Pival

Lexington, Kentucky

Contents

PROBLEM

If a man loses his reverence for any part of life, he will lose his reverence for all of life. —Albert Schweitzer

We cannot command nature except by obeying her. —Francis Bacon

The chief product of the future society is destined to be not food, not things but the quality of the society itself. —Max Ways

A man is rich in proportion to the number of things he can afford to let alone. —Henry David Thoreau

We travel together, passengers on a little spaceship, dependent on its vulnerable reserves of air and soil; all committed for our safety to its security and peace; preserved from annihilation only by the care, the work, and the love we give our fragile craft. —Adlai Stevenson

The renewal of life is the burden and challenge of our time. —Lewis Mumford

Our New Awareness of the Great Web

BY WILLIAM BOWEN

Predictions about anything much less predictable than the rising of the sun are likely to be wrong, or at least seem wrong in hindsight. So we may assume that most predictions put forward in 1937, like those of other years, would now be worth recalling only as examples of fallibility. But at least one prediction published in that year has since come to seem exceedingly perspicacious. It appeared in a book by Kenneth Burke, a literary critic. "Among the sciences," he wrote, "there is one little fellow named Ecology, and in time we shall pay him more attention."

Quite a few years passed before Burke's prophecy was borne out. As recently as 1962 the naturalist Marston Bates wrote: "Ecology may well be the most important of the sciences from the viewpoint of long-term human survival, but it is among those least understood by the general public . . ." Even a year or two ago, anyone not a biologist or a biology student could easily go for months on end without encountering any mention of ecology.

But now, almost suddenly it seems, ecology is popping out all over —the word, at least, if not the science. We meet ecology at dinner parties, in newspaper editorials, on the covers of magazines, in speeches by public officials, at gatherings of scholars in fields remote from biology, and in the names of recently born or reborn corporations (Ecological Science Corp., Ecologic Resources Corp., Ecology Inc.). At this rate,

William Bowen is the Assistant Managing Editor of *Fortune* magazine. He studied history at Princeton and at Yale Graduate School, went to work for *Time* magazine in 1949, and has been a journalist ever since. He has written numerous articles and has long been fascinated with the study of nature.

ecology can be expected to debut before long in *Playboy*, the manifestoes of student rebels, the public utterances of Edward Kennedy, subway-station graffiti, and catch-breeze book titles—*You and Ecology* and perhaps even *Ecology and the Single Girl*. There is an element of fad, of course, in this swift transformation of a mossy scientific term into a conspicuous In word. But there appears to be something much more important, too: what Kenneth Burke foresaw, awakened perception by a great many people of an urgent practical need for the kinds of information, insights, and concepts embraced in ecology.

The term ecology was coined a hundred years ago by the German biologist Ernst Haeckel. The eco-, from the Greek *oikos* (house), is the same eco- as in economics, and according to an old definition, what ecologists study is "the economy of animals and plants." In the now-standard definition, ecology is the science of the relations between organisms and their environment.

That will do as a working definition if we bear in mind that neither in nature nor in the thinking of ecologists are there two distinct compartments, organisms and environment. For any organism, other organisms constitute part of the environment. And the physical environment itself is largely created and maintained by organisms. Atmospheric oxygen, necessary to the survival of life on earth, is itself a product of life, slowly accumulated from the transpiration of aquatic organisms and terrestrial plants. A hardwood forest can maintain its stability for many centuries on end because it creates its own peculiar environment, in which seedlings of only certain plant species can grow to maturity. Recognizing that organisms and their physical environment are interacting parts of a system, an ecologist uses the term "ecosystem" to mean the community of living things and the physical environment, both together, in the segment of nature he is studying.

Ecologists study all kinds of segments, great and small. One ecologist may investigate how various species of mites coexist in the pine-needle litter on a forest floor by occupying separate "niches," or ways of making a living. (It is a well-established principle of ecology that only one species can occupy a particular niche in any habitat.) Another ecologist may work out the intermeshed food chains of various species in a pond or a forest. Still another, a worker in the sprawling, almost unbounded field called "human ecology," may trace the paths by which radioactive substances and persistent pesticides, created by our interventions in nature, accumulate in the tissues of our bodies.

In the diverse studies of ecologists, certain basic themes keep recurring. Together, they may be regarded as the compressed wisdom of ecology.

INTERDEPENDENCE

"The first law of ecology," biologist Barry Commoner remarked not long ago, "is that everything is related to everything else." The continued functioning of any organism depends upon the interlinked functionings of many other organisms. Seemingly autonomous man ultimately depends upon photosynthesis for his food. The seemingly autonomous oak in the forest depends upon microscopic organisms to break down fallen leaves, releasing nutrients that can be absorbed by its roots. Interrelations between organisms are often intricate, and some obscure species provide vital linkages not at all apparent to the casual observer. The seeds of the bitterbush, an important food plant for browsing animals in arid sections of Africa, fail to germinate unless several seeds are buried close together below the surface of the soil; that happens in nature only through the intervention of a species of ground squirrel, which buries hoards of seeds and often forgets them. It is unwise ever to assume that a species is entirely dispensable.

LIMITATION

The saying that trees do not grow to the sky expresses another basic theme of ecology. Nothing grows indefinitely—no organism, no species. Much more commonly than non-ecologists might suppose, animal species limit their own growth: rates of reproduction respond to crowding or other signals so that total numbers remain commensurate with the resources of the ecosystem. In the overall ecosystem of the earth, an outer limit to total animal energy is established by the amount of solar energy plants embody in organic compounds.

COMPLEXITY

When he looks closely at any ecosystem, the ecologist invariably comes upon complexity, an intricate web of interrelations. A diagram showing the movement of a single chemical element through an ecosystem can get exceedingly complicated. In the ecosystem of man, which includes institutions and artifacts that themselves impinge upon and alter the environment, the interrelations are unimaginably complex. This great web, an ecologist said, "is not only more complex than we think. It is more complex than we *can* think."

In their complexity, ecosystems exhibit some of the characteristics of complex systems that Professor Jay W. Forrester of M.I.T. pointed to in *Fortune* ("Overlooked Reasons for Our Social Troubles," December, 1969). In ecosystems as in social systems, causes and effects are often widely separated in both time and space. Accordingly, our interventions often yield unexpected consequences.

After years of spraying persistent pesticides to kill insects, we find that we have come close to wiping out a national symbol, the bald eagle: concentrated through food chains, pesticides accumulate in the tissues of eagles and certain other birds to the point of impairing reproduction. We drain Florida swamplands and learn later on that by reducing the outflow of fresh water into estuaries we have increased their salinity and thereby damaged valuable breeding environments for fish and shrimp. The Aswan Dam impounds silt that would otherwise be carried downstream, so the Nile no longer performs as richly as before its ancient function of renewing fields along its banks. The fertility of the Nile Valley is therefore declining. That is only one variety of ecological backlash from this triumph of engineering. With the flow of the river reduced, salt water is backing into the Nile delta, harming farmlands there. And in time, some authorities predict, the flow of Nile water to new farmlands through irrigation canals will bring on a calamitous spread of schistosomiasis, a liver disease produced by parasites that spend part of their life cycle in the bodies of snails.

Professor Garrett Hardin of the University of California pithily expressed the principal lesson of all this in pointing out that "we can never do merely one thing." When we intervene in a complex system so as to produce a certain desired effect, we always get in addition some other effect or effects, usually not desired. As Hardin also said: "Systems analysis points out in the clearest way the virtual irrelevance of good intentions in determining the consequences of altering a system."

Ecologists are accustomed to looking at nature as a system, and if we had paid more attention to them we might have been spared a lot of backlash. In trying to reduce insect damage to crops, for example, we might have made more use of specific biological or biochemical means of control and less use of persistent broad-spectrum insecticides. We might now, accordingly, have more birds in our countryside and less DDT in our streams—and in some places, fewer harmful insects in our fields.

The recurrent themes of ecology run counter to some old ways of perceiving and thinking that are deeply ingrained in the prevalent world view of Western man. We believe in limitless growth (or did until recently); ecology tells us all growth is limited. We speak (or spoke until recently) of man's "conquest" of nature; ecology tells us we are dependent for our well-being and even survival upon systems in which nature obeys not our rules but its own. Our scientists and engineers, and our social scientists too, proceed by isolating and simplifying; ecology tells us to heed existent complexity and patiently try to trace out its strands. In a sense, then, ecology is subversive. The ecologist Paul B. Sears, a few years ago, called it "a subversive subject," and the editors of a recent compilation of essays on the ecology of man entitled their book *The Subversive Science.*°

In the recent popularity of the word "ecology," therefore, we may be witnessing a sign of momentous historical change. Alterations in the ways men perceive and think about reality lead to alterations in the goals and modes of action. It is too early to tell whether an enduring shift to ecological ways of perceiving and thinking is now in progress, but if it is, the effects will surely be beneficial, on balance. Ecology can help us cope with the environmental ills that beset us, if only by enabling us to avoid bringing on new unintended consequences in trying to remedy old unintended consequences.

Less obviously, ecological thinking can help us cope with the social ills that also insistently press upon us. The social sciences are proving to be inadequate as guides to policy, and the inadequacy is inherent in the prevalent methods and mind-sets of social scientists. In general, they have aped the successful methodology of the physical sciences, but in the study of complex social systems, simplification too readily slides into oversimplification. The social sciences would benefit greatly —and so would we all—by borrowing from the ecologists their willingness to accept and try to puzzle out complexity and their habit of sustained, open-eyed observation of what actually goes on.

For Discussion and Review

1. What do ecologists mean by the term *ecosystem*? What do ecosystems and social systems have in common?
2. Near the end of his essay Bowen states that if we had listened to ecologists, we might have used biological or biochemical means of control rather than insecticides. In view of what he previously said about interdependence and complexity, wouldn't these other measures also have created problems from imbalances? Explain.
3. Bowen argues that the social sciences would do well to adopt the larger perspective of ecology in their analyses of complex systems. If a social scientist followed Bowen's suggestion in analyzing, for example, the causes of an urban riot, what kinds of errors might he avoid? What difficulties would he encounter?
4. Bowen cites several examples to show how intervention into a complex system causes unexpected consequences. What other examples could he have used to make his point?

°Edited by Paul Shepard and Daniel McKinley and published by Houghton Mifflin Company. The book is a rich trove, hard digging in places, but worth it.

The Historical Roots of Our Ecologic Crisis

BY LYNN WHITE, JR.

The victory of Christianity over paganism was the greatest psychic revolution in the history of our culture. It has become fashionable today to say that, for better or worse, we live in "the post-Christian age." Certainly the forms of our thinking and language have largely ceased to be Christian, but to my eye the substance often remains amazingly akin to that of the past. Our daily habits of action, for example, are dominated by an implicit faith in perpetual progress which was unknown either to Greco-Roman antiquity or to the Orient. It is rooted in, and is indefensible apart from, Judeo-Christian teleology. The fact that Communists share it merely helps to show what can be demonstrated on many other grounds: that Marxism, like Islam, is a Judeo-Christian heresy. We continue today to live, as we have lived for about 1700 years, very largely in a context of Christian axioms.

What did Christianity tell people about their relations with the environment?

While many of the world's mythologies provide stories of creation, Greco-Roman mythology was singularly incoherent in this respect. Like Aristotle, the intellectuals of the ancient West denied that the visible world had had a beginning. Indeed, the idea of a beginning was impossible in the framework of their cyclical notion of time. In

Lynn White, Jr., is currently Professor of History at the University of California in Los Angeles. Formerly, he taught at Stanford and Princeton and was President of Mills College. He has written several books on education and technology, including *Machine ex Deo: Essays in the Dynamism of Western Culture, Expansion of Technology, 500-1500,* and *Medieval Technology and Social Change.*

Lynn White, Jr., "The Historical Roots of Our Ecologic Crisis," *Science,* 155 (March 10, 1967), 1203–1207. Copyright 1967 by the American Association for the Advancement of Science. Reprinted by permission of *Science* and the author.

sharp contrast, Christianity inherited from Judaism not only a concept of time as nonrepetitive and linear but also a striking story of creation. By gradual stages a loving and all-powerful God had created light and darkness, the heavenly bodies, the earth and all its plants, animals, birds, and fishes. Finally, God had created Adam and, as an after-thought, Eve, to keep man from being lonely. Man named all the animals, thus establishing his dominance over them. God planned all of this explicitly for man's benefit and rule: no item in the physical creation had any purpose save to serve man's purposes. And, although man's body is made of clay, he is not simply part of nature: he is made in God's image.

Especially in its Western form, Christianity is the most anthropo-centric religion the world has seen. As early as the second century both Tertullian and Saint Irenaeus of Lyons were insisting that when God shaped Adam he was foreshadowing the image of the Incarnate Christ, the Second Adam. Man shares, in great measure, God's tran-scendence of nature. Christianity, in absolute contrast to ancient paganism and Asia's religions (except, perhaps, Zoroastrianism), not only established a dualism of man and nature but also insisted that it is God's will that man exploit nature for his proper ends.

At the level of the common people this worked out in an interesting way. In antiquity every tree, every spring, every stream, every hill had its own *genius loci,* its guardian spirit. These spirits were accessible to men, but were very unlike men; centaurs, fauns, and mermaids show their ambivalence. Before one cut a tree, mined a mountain, or dammed a brook, it was important to placate the spirit in charge of that particular situation, and to keep it placated. By destroying pagan animism, Christianity made it possible to exploit nature in a mood of indifference to the feelings of natural objects.

It is often said that for animism the Church substituted the cult of saints. True; but the cult of saints is functionally quite different from animism. The saint is not *in* natural objects; he may have special shrines, but his citizenship is in heaven. Moreover, a saint is entirely a man; he can be approached in human terms. In addition to saints, Christianity of course also had angels and demons inherited from Judaism and perhaps, at one remove, from Zoroastrianism. But these were all as mobile as the saints themselves. The spirits *in* natural ob-jects, which formerly had protected nature from man, evaporated. Man's effective monopoly on spirit in this world was confirmed, and the old inhibitions to the exploitation of nature crumbled.

When one speaks in such sweeping terms, a note of caution is in order. Christianity is a complex faith, and its consequences differ in differing contexts. What I have said may well apply to the medieval West, where in fact technology made spectacular advances. But the

Greek East, a highly civilized realm of equal Christian devotion, seems to have produced no marked technological innovation after the late seventh century, when Greek fire was invented. The key to the contrast may perhaps be found in a difference in the tonality of piety and thought which students of comparative theology find between the Greek and the Latin churches. The Greeks believed that sin was intellectual blindness, and that salvation was found in illumination, orthodoxy—that is, clear thinking. The Latins, on the other hand, felt that sin was moral evil, and that salvation was to be found in right conduct. Eastern theology has been intellectualist. Western theology has been voluntarist. The Greek saint contemplates; the Western saint acts. The implications of Christianity for the conquest of nature would emerge more easily in the Western atmosphere.

The Christian dogma of creation, which is found in the first clause of all the Creeds, has another meaning for our comprehension of today's ecologic crisis. By revelation, God had given man the Bible, the Book of Scripture. But since God had made nature, nature also must reveal the divine mentality. The religious study of nature for the better understanding of God was known as natural theology. In the early Church, and always in the Greek East, nature was conceived primarily as a symbolic system through which God speaks to men: the ant is a sermon to sluggards; rising flames are the symbol of the soul's aspiration. This view of nature was essentially artistic rather than scientific. While Byzantium preserved and copied great numbers of ancient Greek scientific texts, science as we conceive it could scarcely flourish in such an ambience.

However, in the Latin West by the early thirteenth century natural theology was following a very different bent. It was ceasing to be the decoding of the physical symbols of God's communication with man and was becoming the effort to understand God's mind by discovering how his creation operates. The rainbow was no longer simply a symbol of hope first sent to Noah after the Deluge: Robert Grosseteste, Friar Roger Bacon, and Theodoric of Freiberg produced startlingly sophisticated work on the optics of the rainbow, but they did it as a venture in religious understanding. From the thirteenth century onward, up to and including Leibnitz and Newton, every major scientist, in effect, explained his motivations in religious terms. Indeed, if Galileo had not been so expert an amateur theologian he would have got into far less trouble: the professionals resented his intrusion. And Newton seems to have regarded himself more as a theologian than as a scientist. It was not until the late eighteenth century that the hypothesis of God became unnecessary to many scientists.

It is often hard for the historian to judge, when men explain why they are doing what they want to do, whether they are offering real reasons or merely culturally acceptable reasons. The consistency with which scientists during the long formative centuries of Western science said that the task and the reward of the scientist was "to think God's thoughts after him" leads one to believe that this was their real motivation. If so, then modern Western science was cast in a matrix of Christian theology. The dynamism of religious devotion, shaped by the Judeo-Christian dogma of creation, gave it impetus.

We would seem to be headed toward conclusions unpalatable to many Christians. Since both science and technology are blessed words in our contemporary vocabulary, some may be happy at the notions, first, that, viewed historically, modern science is an extrapolation of natural theology, and, second, that modern technology is at least partly to be explained as an occidental, voluntarist realization of the Christian dogma of man's transcendence of, and rightful mastery over, nature. But, as we now recognize, somewhat over a century ago science and technology—hitherto quite separate activities—joined to give mankind powers which, to judge by many of the ecologic effects, are out of control. If so, Christianity bears a huge burden of guilt.

I personally doubt that disastrous ecologic backlash can be avoided simply by applying to our problems more science and more technology. Our science and technology have grown out of Christian attitudes toward man's relation to nature which are almost universally held not only by Christians and neo-Christians but also by those who fondly regard themselves as post-Christians. Despite Copernicus, all the cosmos rotates around our little globe. Despite Darwin, we are *not*, in our hearts, part of the natural process. We are superior to nature, contemptuous of it, willing to use it for our slightest whim. The newly elected governor of California, [Ronald Reagan], like myself a churchman, but less troubled than I, spoke for the Christian tradition when he said (as is alleged), "when you've seen one redwood tree, you've seen them all." To a Christian a tree can be no more than a physical fact. The whole concept of the sacred grove is alien to Christianity and to the ethos of the West. For nearly two millennia Christian missionaries have been chopping down sacred groves, which are idolatrous because they assume spirit in nature.

What we do about ecology depends on our ideas of the man-nature relationship. More science and more technology are not going to get us out of the present ecologic crisis until we find a new religion, or rethink our old one. The beatniks, who are the basic revolutionaries of our time, show a sound instinct in their affinity for Zen Buddhism, which conceives of the man-nature relationship as very nearly the mirror image of the Christian view. Zen, however, is as deeply conditioned by Asian history as Christianity is by the experience of the West, and I am dubious of its viability among us.

Possibly we should ponder the greatest radical in Christian history since Christ: Saint Francis of Assisi. The prime miracle of Saint Francis is the fact that he did not end at the stake, as many of his left-wing followers did. He was so clearly heretical that a general of the Franciscan Order, Saint Bonaventura, a great and perceptive Christian, tried to suppress the early accounts of Franciscanism. The key to an understanding of Francis is his belief in the virtue of humility—not merely for the individual but for man as a species. Francis tried to depose man from his monarchy over creation and set up a democracy of all God's creatures. With him the ant is no longer simply a homily for the lazy, flames a sign of the thrust of the soul toward union with God; now they are Brother Ant and Sister Fire, praising the Creator in their own ways as Brother Man does in his.

Later commentators have said that Francis preached to the birds as a rebuke to men who would not listen. The records do not read so: he urged the little birds to praise God, and in spiritual ecstasy they flapped their wings and chirped rejoicing. Legends of saints, especially the Irish saints, had long told of their dealings with animals but always, I believe, to show their human dominance over creatures. With Francis it is different. The land around Gubbio in the Apennines was being ravaged by a fierce wolf. Saint Francis, says the legend, talked to the wolf and persuaded him of the error of his ways. The wolf repented, died in the odor of sanctity, and was buried in consecrated ground.

What Sir Steven Ruciman calls "the Franciscan doctrine of the animal soul" was quickly stamped out. Quite possibly it was in part inspired, consciously or unconsciously, by the belief in reincarnation held by the Cathar heretics who at that time teemed in Italy and southern France, and who presumably had got it originally from India. It is significant that at just the same moment, about 1200, traces of metempsychosis are found also in western Judaism, in the Provençal *Cabbala*. But Francis held neither to transmigration of souls nor to pantheism. His view of nature and of man rested on a unique sort of pan-psychism of all things animate and inanimate, designed for the glorification of their transcendent Creator, who, in the ultimate gesture of cosmic humility, assumed flesh, lay helpless in a manger, and hung dying on a scaffold.

I am not suggesting that many contemporary Americans who are concerned about our ecologic crisis will be either able or willing to counsel with wolves or exhort birds. However, the present increasing disruption of the global environment is the product of a dynamic technology and science which were originating in the Western medieval world against which Saint Francis was rebelling in so original a way. Their growth cannot be understood historically apart from distinctive attitudes toward nature which are deeply grounded in Christian dogma. The fact that most people do not think of these attitudes as Christian is irrelevant. No new set of basic values has been accepted in our society to displace those of Christianity. Hence we shall continue to have a worsening ecologic crisis until we reject the Christian axiom that nature has no reason for existence save to serve man.

The greatest spiritual revolutionary in Western history, Saint Francis, proposed what he thought was an alternative Christian view of nature and man's relation to it: he tried to substitute the idea of the equality of all creatures, including man, for the idea of man's limitless rule of creation. He failed. Both our present science and our present technology are so tinctured with orthodox Christian arrogance toward nature that no solution for our ecologic crisis can be expected from them alone. Since the roots of our trouble are so largely religious, the remedy must also be essentially religious, whether we call it that or not. We must rethink and refeel our nature and destiny. The profoundly religious, but heretical, sense of the primitive Franciscans for the spiritual autonomy of all parts of nature may point a direction. I propose Francis as a patron saint for ecologists.

For Discussion and Review

1. What is the thesis of Lynn White's essay? How is the Biblical account of creation related to that thesis?
2. White states that we need either to formulate a new religion or to rethink the old one. Give the reasons why you agree or disagree. If we could revise Judeo-Christian thought, what changes would have to be made to satisfy White's requirements?
3. Do you think the belief in perpetual progress is as widespread today as it was in 1967 when White wrote his essay? Why or why not?
4. Why do you think the author recommends the teachings of St. Francis rather than Zen Buddhism as a basis for a new attitude toward nature? What parallels, if any, could be drawn between the pagan attitude toward nature and that of St. Francis?

Control of Population

BY ROBERT ARDREY

In 1932 the director of the New York Aquarium, C. M. Breder, Jr., working with a colleague, performed an experiment with those small fish known as guppies that shook no worlds. Their conclusions were published in a little-read scientific journal, *Copeia*, and few people today are aware of their work. Yet the 51 guppies who participated in Breder's adventure should one day be memorialized by some watery monument, for they have threatened with ruin a scientific doctrine as unquestioned as any in our time.

There are few of us unfamiliar with the tiny fish so common in our children's aquaria. Guppies multiply lavishly and are born in a ratio of two females for every male. Breder arranged two tanks of equal size, each with an abundant food supply and aeration ample to tolerate a host of fish. Then in one tank he placed 50 guppies with an unnatural distribution of approximately one third males, one third females and the remainder juveniles. In the other tank he placed a single gravid female—one heavy with eggs already fertilized. What he expected to happen, I do not know. What happened defied prediction then, as it defies explanation today.

A remarkable character of the pregnant female guppy is that a single fertilization may give as many as five broods, born every 28 days. The lone gravid female cooperated nobly with the experiment, producing broods as high as 25. Yet at the end of six months there

Robert Ardrey, a controversial writer and anthropologist, has written three books dealing with the behavioral parallels between men and animals: *The African Genesis*; *The Territorial Imperative*; and *The Social Contract*. His other works include seven plays and numerous radio and movie scripts.

From *The Social Contract* by Robert Ardrey. Copyright © 1970 by Robert Ardrey. Reprinted by permission of Atheneum Publishers.

remained only nine fish in her tank. She had eaten the surplus young. In the meantime the tank with an original population of 50 had witnessed a rapid and immediate die-off. No newborn survived. Cannibalism of the young was so active that it was seldom witnessed. The fish surviving at the end of five months were all from the original population. Here too there were nine. And in both tanks there were three males and six females, the ordained proportion among guppies.

An ironic turn in the history of science took place when both Charles Darwin and Alfred Russel Wallace found their inspiration for natural selection in Malthusian doctrine, a thesis which sooner or later must be accepted as in large part false. Thomas Malthus was an English economist who in 1798 published his *Essay on Population*, demonstrating that while human populations multiply—increase, in other words, at geometric pace—food supply can increase only by addition. The number of the population must therefore increase until at some point it overtakes the supply of food. At that point, according to Malthus, the population will reach its limits.

Darwin and Wallace saw in the Malthusian doctrine a natural law which must apply to all animal species. They deduced that through competition for a limited resource, food, selection must take place between the fit and the unfit. The Malthusian logic seemed inarguable. And yet out of the revolution that has so recently overtaken biology, no proposition is more demonstrable than the natural control of animal numbers. Rare is the animal population, unafflicted by climatic catastrophe, that has ever expanded until it reached the limits of its food supply. Rare are the individuals who directly compete for food. An infinite variety of self-regulatory mechanisms, physiological and behavioral, provide that animal numbers—except in the case of climatic catastrophe—will never challenge the carrying capacity of the environment. Population control is the law of the species.

Fifty-one guppies, controlling their numbers through a blend of infanticide and cannibalism, can scarcely be regarded as furnishing a sufficient case for the toppling of Malthus. But as we inquire among species drawn from many a quarter of animal life, the conviction must grow that self-regulation of numbers expresses the law of nature. By one means or another—reduction of litter size, spontaneous abortion, parental neglect, genetic deterioration, even, when other means fail, death by stress—breeding populations are limited. And as the law governs animal groups, we shall see that it governs primitive human societies as well. Civilized man will do well to take notice.

Among all the devices limiting a population, the necessity for a breeding territory is among the most common. A portion of the earth's surface exclusively your own brings you as the proprietor many a material benefit. You are defended, since you know it better than do your enemies. Possession in some strange way enhances your energies and so, through a process of animal justice, sheer might no longer makes right, and on your home grounds you are capable of resisting intruders mightier than you are. Territory may insure a food supply for you and yours. These are benefits accruing to the proprietor, but there are two other powerful benefits accruing to the population and the species. By the physical separation of individuals or groups, dangerous aggressive forces are reduced to shouted insults over common boundaries. And the distribution of available space among breeding couples or groups means that the number of offspring will remain below the carrying capacity of the environment.

Only in recent years has the relation of territory to population numbers become accepted. Even in 1956 Cambridge's eminent ethologist Robert Hinde rejected the proposition as unproved.

Hinde's objection had real grounds: while the necessary possession of a territory quite obviously distributes breeding pairs throughout an environment, it does not follow that territory limits the numbers of such pairs. Space is seldom that confined. To meet the objection, Adam Watson at the University of Aberdeen set up an experiment with red grouse in the Scottish moor.

The problem was to demonstrate that the territorial necessity actually eliminates healthy adult birds from the breeding population. Red grouse males establish territories in the autumn, holding them till the following summer. Space for breeding in the moorland is truly unlimited, yet the competition for territories takes place only in restricted areas. Watson began by selecting a study area and marking all birds in the vicinity. He then cleared 119 territories by capturing or shooting the proprietors. Within a week 111 of the 119 were filled by new males, only a dozen of whom were of unknown origin. All the rest had come from the marked population of the vicinity which constituted a nonbreeding reserve. All bred successfully the following spring. Watson had demonstrated that at least in the red grouse it is the shortage of breeding territories that limits the breeding population.

The most prevalent of all territorial arrangements was first thoroughly demonstrated in 1920 by Eliot Howard's observation of countless species of finches and buntings, warblers, lapwings and woodpeckers in which the female is sexually unresponsive to an unpropertied male. But further research demonstrated the converse of Howard's proposition: the unpropertied or dominated male, in the phrase of the American zoologist A. M. Guhl, tends to be "psychologically castrated." Thus not only does female sexuality guarantee that breeding will be accomplished within a select circle, but sexual inhibition provides that the disenfranchised male will break up no homes.

We still have no certain answer concerning the physiological linking of territorial behavior and the sexual impulse. But the explosion of field research proceeding today leaves no doubt about its reality. In 1966, when I first wrote about the territorial imperative, only one species of African antelope seemed to fit the pattern earlier observed in birds. This was the Uganda kob, a species in which males occupy an arena of territorial competition and to which females are attracted for copulation. Females will accept no others than the successful males, and the masses of surplus males amuse themselves in their bachelor herds. In the few short years since I published my review, territorial systems of breeding have been described in the waterbuck, in the Grant's and Thomson's gazelles and the comparable southern springbok, in the hartebeest and topi and puku and in the smallest of them all, the oribi and dik-dik and steinbok. Systems vary, from the modified arena competition of the wildebeest and puku to the birdlike family territories of the steinbok. But all the main propositions hold true: the female will be attracted only by a territorial male; the male who has failed in the territorial competition will retire into the careless existence of males in groups.

In many a species, of course, the territorial compulsion is absent or fails sufficiently in itself to reduce breeding. Such a force as neglect of offspring may come into play. While parental neglect may seem to the human observer an unappealing means of keeping down numbers, still if we inspect the African lion and its prey, the wildebeest, we shall glimpse a systematic contribution to natural balances.

The wildebeest, one of the most common and certainly the most grotesque of African antelopes, possesses no social organization worthy of analysis excepting the incidence of territorial bulls who maintain a monopoly on copulation. Beyond that, wildebeest, like schools of fish, congregate in immense, disorganized herds, offering the lion his favorite dish, and migrate with the rains, in the hundreds of thousands. And population control takes place in an adjustment of unlikely instincts. The mother drops her calf without more emotional engagement than might take place with a bowel movement. But the calf has an instinct to follow its mother. Miraculously, the newly born wildebeest within five minutes can stagger to its feet and follow. Having identified her calf through its following, the mother will lick it and proceed to recognize it as her own. What, however, happens when herds are so dense that the unfortunate newborn after five minutes cannot recognize its mother? Let it make a wrong guess in the confusions of a wildebeest Times Square. The nonmother will butt it away. The mob will swallow the calf's identity. Lost, unprotected, it must in the end fall to the hyena or jackal.

The lion, preyed on by none, not very susceptible to disease or parasites, could in a few generations be a victim of overpopulation. The lioness produces her several cubs in a short period of gestation, and should she lose them comes into heat again immediately. Yet on Tanzania's great Serengeti Plain a stable population of about a thousand lions varies little in number from season to season. The area's immense numbers of prey animals, such as wildebeest, Thomson's gazelle and zebra, could support far more lions. What keeps their numbers down? A subtle combination of behavior patterns, foremost among them maternal neglect, provides that only so many lions will reach a breeding age and situation.

The first control is territorial. Only those females who are part of a permanently resident pride breed successfully. The second control is a dominant order like few other species. The young eat last. With George Schaller, our foremost student of dangerous animals, I once watched a zebra-kill where nine lionesses, rumbling at each other with the collective menace of a volcano, ringed the carcass flank to flank. In 90 minutes they ate some 450 pounds of meat, while a lone cub on the outskirts played with the zebra's tail which he had somehow managed to secure. Had he sought a single bite before the lionesses were finished, quite probably he would have been killed.

This rank order of feeding, which places the males first, if they are present, the females second and the cubs last, compels no great deprivation so long as large game is available. A wildebeest or zebra will provide food for all. But through the dry season comes a food shortage of a technical nature. The larger game migrates out of the grasslands into the woodlands. The breeding prides refuse to leave their territories and follow. Through the dry season they live off the non-migrating animals, chiefly Thomson's gazelle—and a Tommy weighs only about 45 pounds. Adult appetite is seldom sated, and cubs go hungry. There is little wonder that infant mortality runs to about 50%. Should you in August glimpse two wan cubs waiting while their mother goes hunting, you may be fairly sure that only one will remain in November when the rains and the big game return. Yet food exists in plenty scarcely 50 miles away.

The great majority of animal species, whether through territorial spacing or sexual inhibition, through infanticide or systematic neglect, succeed in maintaining stable populations year after year. But there are those that fail and, to keep numbers in order, must suffer the more drastic solution of cyclical population crashes. With a prayerful thought for our own species, let us consider just what happens to them.

The morbid activities of the lemming have been tantalizing the human imagination for centuries. About every 3 to 5 years, under the sway of some mysterious compulsion, he commits mass suicide.

As recently as 1963 Sweden witnessed one of the greatest "lemming years" in decades. Lapps in the far north first reported the disappearance of lemmings in the month of August. Originating in the mountains, they vanished moving south. They moved mostly at night, and observers at a crossroad counted 44 pass per minute: they moved as individuals, not as groups. Although food was abundant, if one died he was immediately eaten by others, the skull being opened neatly and the brain being eaten first. Of several hundred taken and examined, almost all proved to be the young of the year, and although sexually mature not a female was pregnant. The migration was a youth movement. At any water obstacle, like a lake, they massed on the beaches in such number that an observer could not move without squashing them. Fair enough swimmers, they were not good enough. From a dead-end peninusla on Lake Storsjon so many obeyed the impulse compelling them that the shores of the lake, the following year, were carpeted with lemming bones.

Generations of zoologists interpreted the lemming die-off in Malthusian terms: that is, populations increased until encountering the limits of food supply, then crashed. But observations revealed that migrations as likely as not occurred in years of abundance when no food shortage existed. . . .

Various hypotheses were advanced, the most persuasive by J. J. Christian, one of today's most earnest investigators. He saw the building up of a population as a time of increasing stress. The increasing number of young, the increasing competition of adults, the increasing number of strangers in a massive, increasingly disorganized population at last brings on a state of exhaustion both psychological and physiological. It is as if the cycle's last winter with its normal hardships sets the stage for the entrance of the last straw. And that last straw comes with the sexual demands of the spring. Everybody drops dead.

Whether or not Christian's hypothesis is correct remains unproved. But it served to shift the emphasis of research from the old food-supply theory to the new investigation of the physiological consequences of social stress in high-density populations. Further evidence from the field emphasized the lethal relationship. Most studies had been made of rodents, particularly susceptible to population crashes. But the shrew, studied in Manitoba tamarack bogs, is an insectivore like the mole. During a population explosion in 1957 the excitability of the animals was such that they lived only four days in captivity. By autumn, and the peak of the explosion, they lived only eight hours.

While limitation of numbers through food supply still has its champions in the sciences, most investigators today are turning to social stress as the factor diminishing numbers long before food resources are exhausted. But a menace of another order may come about in rapidly expanding populations: the weakening of the entire gene pool.

The French zoologist François Bourlière has recorded two illuminating studies of deer. The first occurred on a large plateau in Arizona, where a stable population of 4,000 deer lived in balanced relationship with a fair number of wolves, pumas and coyotes. The effect of predators on a prey population is almost invariably to weed out the sick, the malformed, the deficient. The net consequence, observed again and again, is to keep the prey population healthy. But early in this century men began to slaughter the predators and virtually eliminated them. With the slaughter, the numbers of the deer began to rise. By 1920 there were 60,000, by 1924 over 100,000. Then in a single year it crashed to 40,000 and by 1939 was down to 10,000. Overgrazing and food shortage had undoubtedly contributed to the peak crash, but it could not explain the continued decline.

The other example came about through the efforts of the U.S. government to build up a herd of reindeer as food supply for the local inhabitants of St. Paul, one of the Probilof Islands. Here there were no predators at all to exert a selective pressure on the herd, yet for many years the experiment seemed a huge success. It had begun in the autumn of 1911 when four bucks and 21 does were placed on St. Paul. By 1932 they had increased in number to 523, by 1938 to well over 2,000. But then came what Bourlière described as a cataclysmic decline. By 1950 eight remained.

The only possible conclusion is that failure by any agency to remove the weak and the deficient from the breeding population gradually sapped the vitality of the whole gene pool.

It is a fate many scientists have predicted for the human species.

With ample field material now available, science has begun to shift its attention to the laboratory. A single inspired experiment, confirmed and reconfirmed, is worth our attention.

The house mouse is territorial and the female under conditions of normal density encounters only her male. The experiment, which exhibited what later became known as "the Bruce effect," was first conducted in Britain. A female mouse was impregnated by a male. If within four days she was mounted by a strange male, she aborted. The implication was that of a morality in mice previously unsuspected. But the investigation went further. If the impregnated female even *saw* a strange male within four days, the chances were almost fifty-fifty that she would abort. The final experiment demonstrated that the same failure of pregnancy would come about if she were merely placed in a cage where a strange male had been, and she smelled his recent presence. . . .

The Bruce effect is a form of natural birth control. In all probability comparable effects, of which we are yet unaware, explain in many species the reduction in the number of embryos. But the simple effect of stress due to density cannot alone be responsible for the control of animal numbers.

A frequent observation has been the variation of response to growing density by different groups of quite the same creature, living under quite the same conditions. While all at some point must reach a point of reproductive breakdown, levels of tolerance may differ widely. The difference is probably due to the presence or absence of a very strong leader.

The term "alpha" is frequently used in the study of animal behavior to designate the individual of extraordinary endowment who comes to dominate a social group. He may excel in strength, in intelligence, or perhaps in assurance. It is his capacity to dominate a situation, or for that matter to command his fellows, that so often lends cohesion and stability to the group itself. And it is probably such a social group that lends the greatest resistance to stress.

The relation of rank to stress, however, has its grim side. An over-dominated animal may with small ado lie down and die. Rats, introduced to established groups of fellow rats, suffer persecution and may die within days. In a Glasgow laboratory, one died in ninety minutes. He had no significant wound nor had he suffered the least internal injury. He died of stress.

We know that subordinated animals experience enlargement of the adrenal gland, and under the pressure of sufficient stress through adrenal exhaustion may sink into apathy or death. But a curious quality of the alpha male is his relative invulnerability. The same seems to be true of the alpha female in those species where female rank orders exist. In Australian experiments K. Myers has shown that among rabbits subjected to density pressures it is the low-ranking female who suffers the greatest fetus mortality. We may speculate, then, that the "temperament" of a population may well be determined by the random incidence or absence of a powerful alpha, male or female, whose very presence acts to forestall the disintegration of social organization.

The relative immunity of the alpha and vulnerability of the omega, or lowest-ranking, member of a social order is suggested in a 1968 study of men. In that year our journal *Science* published a medical study of all 270,000 male employees of a major American corporation. The mammoth investigation linked educational background, job achievement, and incidence of coronary heart disease.

The corporation offered, like a perfectly arranged laboratory condition, a single controlled environment. Operating units whether in Georgia or New York State had similar structures, fulfilled similar functions, provided similar jobs. All was directed by a single top management policy with the same system of pensions and security, insurance and medical practices, and perhaps most important, of record-keeping. And the 270,000 case histories provided a sample so large that even small variations from the expectable would have statistical significance. The variations were not small.

From bottom to top in the company's pecking order, the study found that workmen contract coronaries at the rate of 4.33 per thousand per year. Their immediate superiors, the formen, have it slightly worse, 4.52. But supervisors and local area managers drop to 3.91. Then comes a leap. General area managers have a mere 2.85. We then come to the high competitors, the high achievers, the high executives. Coronaries occur at a rate of 1.85, about 40% of the level of workmen. And while we may say that many a coronary customer could have been eliminated before reaching the alpha rank, we must also reckon that the high executives are much older. The report ended up puzzled, but admitting that something biological must be going on.

Something biological was most distinctly going on. But if we continue to deny that the histories of alpha monkeys, of alpha rabbits, of alpha antelopes and alpha fish contribute to our understanding of men, then we shall continue to remain puzzled indefinitely.

Throughout all animal species self-regulatory mechanisms provide that population numbers will never challenge the normal carrying capacity of the physical environment. In that cultural animal, man, contraception becomes a cultural substance for innate behavioral or physiological patterns characteristic of animals.

We may regard it as a pity, perhaps, that our females, so unlike the Uganda kob, are sexually responsive to unpropertied males. We may sigh that our omega males do not cheerfully accept a state of psychological castration. We may with less certainty look askance on the lemming's youth movements, under the stress of intolerable numbers, conducting suicidal marches, or the snowshoe hare's dropping dead; for we may just possibly resort to such lugubrious impulses ourselves one day.

However we may regard in human terms the loss of such innate mechanisms, we cannot blame that loss with entire conviction on the mid-Pleistocene expansion of the human brain. Without doubt the rapid enlargement of our cortical equipment exerted increasing inhibition on old forms of compulsive behavior. Even so, in our more primitive days we substituted social traditions for processes that previously had come naturally.

The American ecologist J. B. Birdsell has shown that by natural increase of numbers the aborigine would have reached the food limitations of Australia in two thousand years. But he was there far longer, and he never came close to running out of food. Disease, territorial spacing of groups, tribal warfare may have made contributions. But the principal factor of population control was infanticide. The evidence is as conclusive in the Eskimo, observed before modern influences had modified his ways, as in the Australian aborigine. Both were hunting peoples with a pressing need for active males. In both, the proportion of young males to females was about 150 to 100. Girl babies had been the chief object of destruction.

The Scottish ecologist V. C. Wynne-Edwards is today our foremost authority on the self-regulation of animal numbers. Almost half a century ago, however, Sir Alexander Carr-Saunders explored the principle as displayed by primitive peoples. At that date he was of course unaware of the long history of animal populations, and he presumed that population control had begun in the Stone Age. His comprehensive review of almost all then known about primitive tribes led to his thesis of "optimum numbers." Within every group there is a number about which population fluctuates only slightly. It is a number well under any threat by starvation, yet sufficient to gain a maximum yield from its environment. The number is sustained by varying traditions—by infanticide or compulsory abortion, by cannibalism, head-hunting, human sacrifice, ritual murder, by taboos against incest or against intercourse during the period of lactation. The environment is held to a constant size either through outright territorial defense, or through traditional attachment to a familiar area. . . .

Throughout a large world of primitive societies, missionaries and colonial masters reacted with horror to such institutions as cannibalism, head-hunting and human sacrifice. Tribal warfare, particularly in Africa, was ended. Infanticide was discouraged.

Then the advent of modern medicine and biochemistry struck also at the advanced countries. The rate of infant mortality dropped like a rock in a well. Life was so prolonged that a new class of senior citizen came into being. Breeding populations were now seldom reduced by the death of a young mother in childbirth. Strangely enough, with modern nutrition in the same countries the onset of menstruation and fecundity dropped two years in less than a century. Through mass-produced drugs and insecticides, we extended the new breeding potential to all peoples, advanced or otherwise.

The humanist's preoccupation with the numbers game has sacrificed human quality for human quantity. Life must be prolonged, whatever agony it presents to the dying. A child defective physically or mentally must somehow be saved sufficiently to join the breeding population. To restrict the reproductive rights of the genetically afflicted is considered an act of discrimination.

We shall find out one day if, as many biologists fear, overprotection of the human being, like underpredation in the reindeer herd on St. Paul Island, will produce a genetic collapse in the most compassionate populations. If so, it will be an appropriate biological conclusion to a valuable if misdirected philosophy. Yet I find it too neat and simple a conclusion.

Let us review the other possibilities. Human numbers will probably never reach such magnitude as to encounter the limitations of food supply. Long before such a rendezvous can take place, other forces will have affected our numbers. If we take nature as a model, there are two probabilities. The first is a sane and humane program of population control. The second is death by stress.

Population control, whatever form it takes, is a cultural substitute for biological mechanisms prevalent in the natural world. As our population problem has a cultural cause, so we are provided with a cultural answer. But that answer must be mandatory. We have seen that in animal species the numbers of young are not determined by parental choice. A number of proposals for the human species have been seriously put forth by population experts. We must consider enforced contraception, whether through taxation on surplus children, or through more severe means such as conception license, replacing or supplementing the marriage license. Abortion should be freely available to those suffering unintended pregnancy. In international relations, of course, any aid to peoples who through ignorance, prejudice or political hypnosis fail to control their numbers might be forbidden.

Such a program sounds more formidable than it would probably prove in practice. The vast majority among us accept traffic regulations without resentment because we are aware of their necessity. Conscience, too, has a way of internalizing what has started with external pressure, and of transferring to the voluntary what was once the compulsory. Even custom makes its contribution, so that what is socially unacceptable becomes something that is simply not done. Most hopeful of all is the demonstrable proposition that a cultural institution which accords with the laws of nature rarely fails. Such is birth control.

Birth control, a solution both sane and humane, has of course its alternative. But the alternative, death by stress, is a messy one indeed. If we recognize that population density, not food supply, is the chief factor limiting animal numbers, and if we recognize also that no population increases indefinitely, then however unattractive or insane the alternative control may be, we may have to accept it. Since a thoroughly savage program is available, let us consider how we may achieve death by stress:

The rising rate of automobile accidents is a quite perfect example of a form of population control mathematically determined by population density. If we accept an insane solution as preferable to a sane one, then we must see that the automobile, which strikes most heavily at the young, is indeed an excellent instrument for reducing the breeding population.

Another agency striking hard at the young is drug addiction. While we cannot yet be sure that drugs reduce reproductive potential, still we should be wise to gamble that they do, or that they reduce the breeding drive. We must offer every encouragement to widespread addiction in the young.

The trouble with cardiac and other stress diseases is that they tend to reduce numbers in those who have passed the breeding age. Even so, we know that the omega is far more susceptible to stress than the alpha. We should therefore encourage in business, for example, tendencies toward mergers and ever-magnifying organizations that reduce in numbers the immune alpha and infinitely expand the ranks of the vulnerable omega.

If life in the megalopolis discourages large families, then perhaps by discriminatory taxation falling most heavily on real estate we might reverse the flight to the suburbs and drive middle-class families back to the unpleasantness of urban reproduction. We should have nothing to lose by such a move, in any case, since further concentrations of city life must produce more stress, more broken marriages, more impotency due to acute alcoholism, more corpses, victims of crime in the streets and more couples living together in unreproductive sin.

Homosexuality should not be neglected. Already it subtracts four to six percent from the American breeding population. We could do better.

Suicide too offers splendid vistas. We fall far behind such advanced peoples as the Swedes and the Swiss. Here too we could do better. But as stress and density increase I feel a confidence—or perhaps it is no more than a vague patriotism—that we Americans will catch up, and that suicide, particularly in the young and the discouraged, will make a significant reduction in our breeding numbers.

What at all times we must keep brightly in mind, as we inspect the real possibilities of death by stress, is that while any reduction in numbers is a gain, significant reduction can only be accomplished in the young breeding group. The reader may wonder, with such an admonition, why I have so ignored war as an instrument. But war, in my opinion, has seen its best days. Its growing unpopularity with those who must fight it may turn out to be a passing whim. More serious is war's increasing preoccupation with the wastage of expensive machinery rather than with the traditional wastage of inexpensive men. Wars simply do not kill enough people. A nuclear entertainment would of course leave us with no population problem at all. But even as highly publicized a war as that in Vietnam has failed throughout its entire course to kill as many Americans as that magnificent engine of destruction, the automobile, kills in a normal year.

We must look to more imaginative agencies than war to dispose of the immense numbers who must someday die of stress. And I am sure that some future survey of likely instruments will reveal lethal possibilities of a wonder that the imagination cannot glimpse today. When our population has again doubled, when not a water supply remains unpolluted, when the traffic jams of tomorrow make today's seem memories of the open road, when civil disorder has permanently replaced war as a form of organized violence, when the air of the city can no longer be breathed and the countryside has vanished, when crime has become so prevalent that no citizen goes unarmed, when indigestion becomes a meal's final course and varieties of rage and frustration remain the only emotions man or woman can know, then perhaps, if we are young, we shall comprehend the lemming.

But of course future times of such stressful wonder may never come to be. Somewhere along the road we may choose compulsory contraception. And yet no one can make a sure prediction. *Homo sapiens,* that creature mad beyond the craziest of hares, lunatic beyond all lemmings, may go to the end of the road with no impulse more logical than to discover what lies there. How high is the mountain, how profound the stream? Which in the end will bend the ultimately defeated knee, we or our world? Shall we embrace the logic of limited numbers, acceptable to mice, or shall we mount the hilltop and defy the winds?

One cannot say. The tragedy and the magnificence of *Homo sapiens* together rise from the same smoky truth that we alone among animal species refuse to acknowledge natural law.

For Discussion and Review

1. Using the example of the reindeer on St. Paul Island, explain how the vitality of an entire gene pool can be weakened. Why do some geneticists fear this may happen to modern man?
2. Peter Freuchen, the author of *Book of the Eskimos*, once related an incident of Eskimo cannibalism which occurred during a winter when the seal catch was extremely poor and a whole group of Hudson Bay Eskimos faced mass starvation. In the spring only a few adults of child-breeding age were left alive, but they refused to speak of their experience. Freuchen inferred that the older people and children had been eaten. Relate this incident to some of the points Ardrey makes in his article.
3. Explain the significance of the alpha-omega study. What other statistical studies of the last ten years have made a great impact on American life? What problems are involved in interpreting statistical studies?
4. Ardrey makes several recommendations for "sane" population control. What arguments have you heard against these suggestions? What ethical and political problems would be involved in implementing these suggestions? How do you feel about compulsory contraception? Legalized abortion? Taxation of large families?

CONTROVERSY

Science is always wrong. It never solves a problem without causing ten more.   —George Bernard Shaw

I want to warn that antipollution is not what we politicians call a "warm puppy" issue, one which if we pass enough laws, spend enough money and have a good heart, happiness is assured and soon America will be beautiful again. Antipollution means that someone will be hurt. Profits must be cut, comforts reduced, taxes raised, sacrifices endured. And, as in all human struggles, the powerful will fight the hardest to be hurt the least.
                                                        —James B. Pearson

In our time the technocrats have the upper hand. Almost everywhere, they have power alignments with the politicians. It is obvious, however, that this trend will be reversed. Biological sciences will in the end take the lead, for without life, there is no science.   —J. Y. Costeau

We all proclaim our love and respect for wild nature, and in the same breath we confess our firm attachment to values that in-inexorably demand the destruction of the last remnant of wilderness.   —Thomas Merton

Eco-Catastrophe

BY PAUL EHRLICH

I

The end of the ocean came late in the summer of 1979, and it came even more rapidly than the biologists had expected. There had been signs for more than a decade, commencing with the discovery in 1968 that DDT slows down photosynthesis in marine plant life. It was announced in a short paper in the technical journal, *Science*, but to ecologists it smacked of doomsday. They knew that all life in the sea depends on photosynthesis, the chemical process by which green plants bind the sun's energy and make it available to living things. And they knew that DDT and similar chlorinated hydrocarbons had polluted the entire surface of the earth, including the sea.

But that was only the first of many signs. There had been the final gasp of the whaling industry in 1973, and the end of the Peruvian anchovy fishery in 1975. Indeed, a score of other fisheries had disappeared quietly from overexploitation and various eco-catastrophes by 1977. The term "eco-catastrophe" was coined by a California ecologist in 1969 to describe the most spectacular of man's attacks on the systems which sustain his life. He drew his inspiration from the Santa Barbara offshore oil disaster of that year, and from the news which spread among naturalists that virtually all of the Golden State's seashore bird life was doomed because of chlorinated hydrocarbon inter-

Paul Ehrlich, formerly a research associate at the Chicago Academy of Science and the University of Kansas, has been Professor of Biological Science at Stanford University for many years. His books include *How to Know the Butterflies*, *The Process of Evolution*, and *The Population Bomb*.

ference with its reproduction. Eco-catastrophes in the sea became increasingly common in the early 1970s. Mysterious "blooms" of previously rare microorganisms began to appear in offshore waters. Red tides—killer outbreaks of a minute single-celled plant—returned to the Florida Gulf coast and were sometimes accompanied by tides of other exotic hues.

It was clear by 1975 that the entire ecology of the ocean was changing. A few types of phytoplankton were becoming resistant to chlorinated hydrocarbons and were gaining the upper hand. Changes in the phytoplankton community led inevitably to changes in the community of zooplankton, the tiny animals which eat the phytoplankton. These changes were passed on up the chains of life in the ocean to the herring, plaice, cod and tuna. As the diversity of life in the ocean diminished, its stability also decreased.

Other changes had taken place by 1975. Most ocean fishes that returned to fresh water to breed, like the salmon, had become extinct, their breeding streams so dammed up and polluted that their powerful homing instinct only resulted in suicide. Many fishes and shellfishes that bred in restricted areas along the coasts followed them as onshore pollution escalated.

By 1977 the annual yield of fish from the sea was down to 30 million metric tons, less than one-half the per capita catch of a decade earlier. This helped malnutrition to escalate sharply in a world where an estimated 50 million people per year were already dying of starvation. The United Nations attempted to get all chlorinated hydrocarbon insecticides banned on a worldwide basis, but the move was defeated by the United States. This opposition was generated primarily by the American petrochemical industry, operating hand in glove with its subsidiary, the United States Department of Agriculture. Together they persuaded the government to oppose the U.N. move—which was not difficult since most Americans believed that Russia and China were more in need of fish products than was the United States. The United Nations also attempted to get fishing nations to adopt strict and enforced catch limits to preserve dwindling stocks. This move was blocked by Russia, who, with the most modern electronic equipment, was in the best position to glean what was left in the sea. It was, curiously, on the very day in 1977 when the Soviet Union announced its refusal that another ominous article appeared in *Science*. It announced that incident solar radiation had been so reduced by worldwide air pollution that serious effects on the world's vegetation could be expected.

II

Apparently it was a combination of ecosystem destablization, sunlight reduction, and a rapid escalation in chlorinated hydrocarbon pollution from massive Thanodrin applications which triggered the ultimate catastrophe. Seventeen huge Soviet-financed Thanodrin plants were operating in underdeveloped countries by 1978. They had been part of a massive Russian "aid offensive" designed to fill the gap caused by the collapse of America's ballyhooed "Green Revolution."

It became apparent in the early '70s that the "Green Revolution" was more talk than substance. Distribution of high yield "miracle" grain seeds had caused temporary local spurts in agricultural production. Simultaneously, excellent weather had produced record harvests. The combination permitted bureaucrats, especially in the United States Department of Agriculture and the Agency for International Development (AID), to reverse their previous pessimism and indulge in an outburst of optimistic propaganda about staving off famine. They raved about the approaching transformation of agriculture in the underdeveloped countries (UDCs). The reason for the propaganda reversal was never made clear. Most historians agree that a combination of utter ignorance of ecology, a desire to justify past errors, and pressure from agro-industry (which was eager to sell pesticides, fertilizers, and farm machinery to the UDCs and agencies helping the UDCs) was behind the campaign. Whatever the motivation, the results were clear. Many concerned people, lacking the expertise to see through the Green Revolution drivel, relaxed. The population-food crisis was "solved."

But reality was not long in showing itself. Local famine persisted in northern India even after good weather brought an end to the ghastly Bihar famine of the mid-'60s. East Pakistan was next, followed by a resurgence of general famine in northern India. Other foci of famine rapidly developed in Indonesia, the Philippines, Malawi, the Congo, Egypt, Colombia, Ecuador, Honduras, the Dominican Republic, and Mexico.

Everywhere hard realties destroyed the illusion of the Green Revolution. Yields dropped as the progressive farmers who had first accepted the new seeds found that their higher yields brought lower prices—effective demand (hunger plus cash) was not sufficient in poor countries to keep prices up. Less progressive farmers, observing this, refused to make the extra effort required to cultivate the "miracle" grains. Transport systems proved inadequate to bring the necessary fertilizer to the fields where the new and extremely fertilizer-sensitive grains were being grown. The same systems were also inadequate to move produce to markets. Fertilizer plants were not built fast enough, and most of the underdeveloped countries could not scrape together funds to purchase supplies, even on concessional terms. Finally, the inevitable happened, and pests began to reduce yields in even the most carefully cultivated fields. Among the first were the famous "miracle rats" which invaded Philippine "miracle rice" fields early in 1969. They were quickly followed by many insects and viruses, thriving on the relatively pest-susceptible new grains, encouraged by the vast and dense plantings, and rapidly acquiring resistance to the chemicals used against them. As chaos spread until even the most obtuse agriculturists and economists realized that the Green Revolution had turned brown, the Russians stepped in.

In retrospect it seems incredible that the Russians, with the American mistakes known to them, could launch an even more incompetent program of aid to the underdeveloped world. Indeed, in the early 1970s there were cynics in the United States who claimed that outdoing the stupidity of American foreign aid would be physically impossible. Those critics were, however, obviously unaware that the Russians had been busily destroying their own environment for many years. The virtual disappearance of sturgeon from Russian rivers caused a great shortage of caviar by 1970. A standard joke among Russian scientists at that time was that they had created an artificial caviar which was indistinguishable from the real thing—except by taste. At any rate the Soviet Union, observing with interest the progressive deterioration of relations between the UDCs and the United States, came up with a solution. It had recently developed what it claimed was the ideal insecticide, a highly lethal chlorinated hydrocarbon complexed with a special agent for penetrating the external skeletal armor of insects. Announcing that the new pesticide, called Thanodrin, would truly produce a Green Revolution, the Soviets entered into negotiations with various UDCs for the construction of massive Thanodrin factories. The USSR would bear all the costs; all it wanted in return were certain trade and military concessions.

It is interesting now, with the perspective of years, to examine in some detail the reasons why the UDCs welcomed the Thanodrin plan with such open arms. Government officials in these countries ignored the protests of their own scientists that Thanodrin would not solve the problems which plagued them. The governments now knew that the basic cause of their problems was overpopulation, and that these problems had been exacerbated by the dullness, daydreaming, and cupidity endemic to all governments. They knew that only population control and limited development aimed primarily at agriculture could have spared them the horrors they now faced. They knew it, but they were not about to admit it. How much easier it was simply to accuse the Americans of failing to give them proper aid; how much simpler to accept the Russian panacea.

And then there was the general worsening of relations between the United States and the UDCs. Many things had contributed to this. The situation in America in the first half of the 1970s deserves our close scrutiny. Being more dependent on imports for raw materials than the Soviet Union, the United States had, in the early 1970s, adopted more and more heavy-handed policies in order to insure continuing supplies. Military adventures in Asia and Latin America had further lessened the international credibility of the United States as a great defender of freedom—an image which had begun to deteriorate rapidly during the pointless and fruitless Vietnam conflict. At home, acceptance of the carefully manufactured image lessened dramatically, as even the more romantic chauvinistic citizens began to understand the role of the military and the industrial system in what John Kenneth Galbraith had aptly named "The New Industrial State."

At home in the USA the early '70s were traumatic times. Racial violence grew and the habitability of the cities diminished, as nothing substantial was done to ameliorate either racial inequities or urban blight. Welfare rolls grew as automation and general technological progress forced more and more people into the category of "unemployable." Simultaneously a taxpayers' revolt occurred. Although there was not enough money to build the schools, roads, water systems, sewage systems, jails, hospitals, urban transit lines, and all the other amenities needed to support a burgeoning population, Americans refused to tax themselves more heavily. Starting in Youngstown, Ohio in 1969 and followed closely by Richmond, California, community after community was forced to close its schools or curtail educational operations for lack of funds. Water supplies, already marginal in quality and quantity in many places by 1970, deteriorated quickly. Water rationing occurred in 1723 municipalities in the summer of 1974, and hepatitis and epidemic dysentery rates climbed about 500 per cent between 1970–1974.

III

Air pollution continued to be the most obvious manifestation of environmental deterioration. It was, by 1972, quite literally in the eyes of all Americans. The year 1973 saw not only the New York and Los Angeles smog disasters, but also the publication of the Surgeon General's massive report on air pollution and health. The public had been partially prepared for the worst by the publicity given to the U.N. pollution conference held in 1972. Deaths in the late '60s caused by smog were well known to scientists, but the public had ignored them because they mostly involved the early demise of the old and sick rather than people dropping dead on the freeways. But suddenly our citizens were faced with nearly 200,000 corpses and massive documentation that they could be the next to die from respiratory disease. They were not ready for that scale of disaster. After all, the U.N. conference had not predicted that accumulated air pollution would make the planet uninhabitable until almost 1990. The population was terrorized as TV screens became filled with scenes of horror from the disaster areas. Especially vivid was NBC's coverage of hundreds of unattended people choking out their lives outside of New York's hospitals. Terms like nitrogen oxide, acute bronchitis, and cardiac arrest began to have real meaning for most Americans.

The ultimate horror was the announcement that chlorinated hydrocarbons were now a major constituent of air pollution in all American cities. Autopsies of smog disaster victims revealed an average chlorinated hydrocarbon load in fatty tissue equivalent to 26 parts per million of DDT. In October, 1973, the Department of Health, Education, and Welfare announced studies which showed unequivocally that increasing death rates from hypertension, cirrhosis of the liver, liver cancer, and a series of other diseases had resulted from the chlorinated hydrocarbon load. They estimated that Americans born since 1946 (when DDT usage began) now had a life expectancy of only 49 years, and predicted that if current patterns continued, this expectancy would reach 42 years by 1980, when it might level out. Plunging insurance stocks triggered a stock market panic. The president of Velsicol, Inc., a major pesticide producer, went on television to "publicly eat a teaspoonful of DDT" (it was really powdered milk) and announce that HEW had been infiltrated by Communists. Other giants of the petrochemical industry, attempting to dispute the indisputable evidence, launched a massive pressure campaign on Congress to force HEW to "get out of agriculture's business." They were aided by the agrochemical journals, which had decades of experience in misleading the public about the benefits and dangers of pesticides. But by now the public realized that it had been duped. The Nobel Prize for medicine and physiology was given to Drs. J. L. Radomski and W. B. Deichmann, who in the late 1960s had pioneered in the documentation of the long-term lethal effects of chlorinated hydrocarbons. A Presidential Commission with unimpeachable credentials directly accused the agro-chemical complex of "condemning many millions of Americans to an early death." The year 1973 was the year in which Americans finally came to understand the direct threat to their existence posed by environmental deterioration.

And 1973 was also the year in which most people finally comprehended the indirect threat. Even the president of Union Oil Company and several other industrialists publicly stated their concern over the reduction of bird populations which had resulted from pollution by DDT and other chlorinated hydrocarbons. Insect populations boomed because they were resistant to most pesticides and had been freed, by the incompetent use of those pesticides, from most of their natural enemies. Rodents swarmed over crops, multiplying rapidly in the absence of predatory birds. The effect of pests on the wheat crop was especially disastrous in the summer of 1973, since that was also the year of the great drought. Most of us can remember the shock which greeted the announcement by atmospheric physicists that the shift of the jet stream which had caused the drought was probably permanent. It signalled the birth of the Midwestern desert. Man's air-polluting activities had by then caused gross changes in climatic patterns. The news, of course, played hell with commodity and stock markets. Food prices skyrocketed, as savings were poured into hoarded canned goods. Official assurances that food supplies would remain ample fell on deaf ears, and even the government showed signs of nervousness when California migrant field workers went out on strike again in protest against the continued use of pesticides by growers. The strike burgeoned into farm burning and riots. The workers, calling themselves "The Walking Dead," demanded immediate compensation for their shortened lives, and crash research programs to attempt to lengthen them.

It was in the same speech in which President Edward Kennedy, after much delay, finally declared a national emergency and called out the National Guard to harvest California's crops, that the first mention of population control was made. Kennedy pointed out that the United States would no longer be able to offer any food aid to other nations and was likely to suffer food shortages herself. He suggested that, in view of the manifest failure of the Green Revolution, the only hope of the UDCs lay in population control. His statement, you will recall, created an uproar in the underdeveloped countries. Newspaper editorials accused the United States of wishing to prevent small countries from becoming large nations and thus threatening American hegemony. Politicians asserted that President Kennedy was a "creature of the giant drug combine" that wished to shove its pills down every woman's throat.

Among Americans, religious opposition to population control was very slight. Industry in general also backed the idea. Increasing poverty in the UDCs was both destroying markets and threatening supplies of raw materials. The seriousness of the raw material situation had been brought home during the Congressional Hard Resources hearings in 1971. The exposure of the ignorance of the cornucopian economists had been quite a spectacle—a spectacle brought into virtually every American's home in living color. Few would forget the distinguished geologist from the University of California who suggested that economists be legally required to learn at least the most elementary facts of geology. Fewer still would forget that an equally distinguished Harvard economist added that they might be required to learn some economics, too. The overall message was clear: America's resource situation was bad and bound to get worse. The hearings had led to a bill requiring the Departments of State, Interior, and Commerce to set up a joint resource procurement council with the express purpose of "insuring that proper consideration of American resource needs be an integral part of American foreign policy."

Suddenly the United States discovered that it had a national consensus: population control was the only possible salvation of the underdeveloped world. But that same consensus led to heated debate. How could the UDCs be persuaded to limit their populations, and should not the United States lead the way by limiting its own? Members of the intellectual community wanted America to set an example. They pointed out that the United States was in the midst of a new baby boom: her birth rate, well over 20 per thousand per year, and her growth rate of over one per cent per annum were among the very highest of the developed countries. They detailed the deterioration of the American physical and psychic environments, the growing health threats, the impending food shortages, and the insufficiency of funds for desperately needed public works. They contended that the nation was clearly unable or unwilling to properly care for the people it already had. What possible reason could there be, they queried, for adding any more? Besides, who would listen to requests by the United States for population control when the nation did not control her own profligate reproduction?

Those who opposed population controls for the U.S. were equally vociferous. The military-industrial complex, with its all-too-human mixture of ignorance and avarice, still saw strength and prosperity in numbers. Baby food magnates, already worried by the growing nitrate pollution of their products, saw their market disappearing. Steel manufacturers saw a decrease in aggregate demand and slippage for that holy of holies, the Gross National Product. And military men saw, in the growing population-food-environment crisis, a serious threat to their carefully nurtured Cold War. In the end, of course, economic arguments held sway, and the "inalienable right of every American couple to determine the size of its family," a freedom invented for the occasion in the early '70s, was not compromised.

The population control bill, which was passed by Congress early in 1974, was quite a document, nevertheless. On the domestic front, it authorized an increase from 100 to 150 million dollars in funds for "family planning" activities. This was made possible by a general feeling in the country that the growing army on welfare needed family planning. But the gist of the bill was a series of measures designed to impress the need for population control on the UDCs. All American aid to countries with overpopulation problems was required by law to consist in part of population control assistance. In order to receive any assistance each nation was required not only to accept the population control aid, but also to match it according to a complex formula. "Overpopulation" itself was defined by a formula based on U.N. statistics, and the UDCs were required not only to accept aid, but also to show progress in reducing birth rates. Every five years the status of the aid program for each nation was to be reevaluated.

The reaction to the announcement of this program dwarfed the response to President Kennedy's speech. A coalition of UDCs attempted to get the U.N. General Assembly to condemn the United States as a "genetic aggressor." Most damaging of all to the American cause was the famous "25 Indians and a dog" speech by Mr. Shankarnarayan, Indian Ambassador to the U.N. Shankarnarayan pointed out that for several decades the United States, with less than six per cent of the people of the world had consumed roughly 50 per cent of the raw materials used every year. He described vividly America's contribution to worldwide environmental deterioration, and he scathingly denounced the miserly record of United States foreign aid as "unworthy of a fourth-rate power, let alone the most powerful nation on earth."

It was the climax of his speech, however, which most historians claim once and for all destroyed the image of the United States. Shankarnarayan informed the assembly that the average American family dog was fed more animal protein per week than the average Indian got in a month. "How do you justify taking fish from protein-starved Peruvians and feeding them to your animals?" he asked. "I contend," he concluded, "that the birth of an American baby is a greater disaster for the world than that of 25 Indian babies." When the applause had died away, Mr. Sorensen, the American representative, made a speech which said essentially that "other countries look after their own self-interest, too." When the vote came, the United States was condemned.

IV

This condemnation set the tone of U.S.-UDC relations at the time the Russian Thanodrin proposal was made. The proposal seemed to offer the masses in the UDCs an opportunity to save themselves and humiliate the United States at the same time; and in human affairs, as we all know, biological realities could never interfere with such an opportunity. The scientists were silenced, the politicians said yes, the Thanodrin plants were built, and the results were what any beginning ecology student could have predicted. At first Thanodrin seemed to offer excellent control of many pests. True, there was a rash of human fatalities from improper use of the lethal chemical, but, as Russian technical advisors were prone to note, these were more than compensated for by increased yields. Thanodrin use skyrocketed throughout the underdeveloped world. The Mikoyan design group developed a dependable, cheap agricultural aircraft which the Soviets donated to the effort in large numbers. MIG sprayers became even more common in UDCs than MIG interceptors.

Then the troubles began. Insect strains with cuticles resistant to Thanodrin penetration began to appear. And as streams, rivers, fish culture ponds and onshore waters became rich in Thanodrin, more fisheries began to disappear. Bird populations were decimated. The sequence of events was standard for broadcast use of a synthetic pesticide: great success at first, followed by removal of natural enemies and development of resistance by the pest. Populations of crop-eating insects in areas treated with Thanodrin made steady comebacks and soon became more abundant than ever. Yields plunged, while farmers in their desperation increased the Thanodrin dose and shortened the time between treatments. Death from Thanodrin poisoning became common. The first violent incident occurred in the Canete Valley of Peru, where farmers had suffered a similar chlorinated hydrocarbon disaster in the mid-'50s. A Russian advisor serving as an agricultural pilot was assaulted and killed by a mob of enraged farmers in January, 1978. Trouble spread rapidly during 1978, especially after the word got out that two years earlier Russia herself had banned the use of Thanodrin at home because of its serious effects on ecological systems. Suddenly Russia, and not the United States, was the *bête noir* in the UDCs. "Thanodrin parties" became epidemic, with farmers, in their ignorance, dumping carloads of Thanodrin concentrate into the sea. Russian advisors fled, and four of the Thanodrin plants were leveled to the ground. Destruction of the plants in Rio and Calcutta led to hundreds of thousands of gallons of Thanodrin concentrate being dumped directly into the sea.

Mr. Shankarnarayan again rose to address the U.N., but this time it was Mr. Potemkin, representative of the Soviet Union, who was on the hot seat. Mr. Potemkin heard his nation described as the greatest mass killer of all time as Shankarnarayan predicted at least 30 million deaths from crop failures due to overdependence on Thanodrin. Russia was accused of "chemical aggression," and the General Assembly, after a weak reply by Potemkin, passed a vote of censure.

It was in January, 1979, that huge blooms of a previously unknown variety of diatom were reported off the coast of Peru. The blooms were accompanied by a massive die-off of sea life and of the pathetic remainder of the birds which had once feasted on the anchovies of the area. Almost immediately another huge bloom was reported in the Indian ocean, centering around the Seychelles, and then a third in the South Atlantic off the African coast. Both of these were accompanied by spectacular die-offs of marine animals. Even more ominous were growing reports of fish and bird kills at oceanic points where there were no spectacular blooms. Biologists were soon able to explain the phenomena: the diatom had evolved an enzyme which broke down Thanodrin; that enzyme also produced a breakdown product which interfered with the transmission of nerve impulses, and was therefore lethal to animals. Unfortunately, the biologists could suggest no way of repressing the poisonous diatom bloom in time. By September, 1979, all important animal life in the sea was extinct. Large areas of coastline had to be evacuated, as windrows of dead fish created a monumental stench.

But stench was the least of man's problems. Japan and China were faced with almost instant starvation from a total loss of the seafood on which they were so dependent. Both blamed Russia for their situation and demanded immediate mass shipments of food. Russia had none to send. On October 13, Chinese armies attacked Russia on a broad front. . . .

V

A pretty grim scenario. Unfortunately, we're a long way into it already. Everything mentioned as happening before 1970 has actually occurred; much of the rest is based on projections of trends already appearing. Evidence that pesticides have long-term lethal effects on human beings has started to accumulate, and recently Robert Finch, Secretary of the Department of Health, Education, and Welfare expressed his extreme apprehension about the pesticide situation. Simultaneously the petrochemical industry continues its unconscionable poison-peddling. For instance, Shell Chemical has been carrying on a high-pressure campaign to sell the insecticide Azodrin to farmers as a killer of cotton pests. They continue their program even though they know that Azodrin is not only ineffective, but often *increases* the pest density. They've covered themselves nicely in an advertisement which states, "Even if an overpowering migration [sic] develops, the flexibility of Azodrin lets you regain control fast. Just increase the dosage according to label recommendations." It's a great game—get people to apply the poison and kill the natural enemies of the pests. Then blame the increased pests on "migration" and sell even more pesticide!

Right now fisheries are being wiped out by overexploitation, made easy by modern electronic equipment. The companies producing the equipment know this. They even boast in advertising that only their equipment will keep fishermen in business until the final kill. Profits must obviously be maximized in the short run. Indeed, Western society is in the process of completing the rape and murder of the planet for economic gain. And, sadly, most of the rest of the world is eager for the opportunity to emulate our behavior. But the underdeveloped peoples will be denied that opportunity—the days of plunder are drawing inexorably to a close.

Most of the people who are going to die in the greatest cataclysm in the history of man have already been born. More than three and a half billion people already populate our moribund globe, and about half of them are hungry. Some 10 to 20 million will starve to death *this year*. In spite of this, the population of the earth will increase by 70 million souls in 1969. For mankind has artificially lowered the death rate of the human population, while in general birth rates have remained high. With the input side of the population system in high gear and the output side slowed down our fragile planet has filled with people at an incredible rate. It took several million years for the population to reach a total of two billion people in 1930, while a *second two billion will have been added by 1975!* By that time some experts feel that food shortages will have escalated the present level of world hunger and starvation into famines of unbelievable proportions. Other experts, more optimistic, think the ultimate food-population collision will not occur until the decade of the 1980s. Of course more massive famine may be avoided if other events cause a prior rise in the human death rate.

Both worldwide plague and thermonuclear war are made more probable as population growth continues. These, along with famine, make up the trio of potential "death rate solutions" to the population problem—solutions in which the birth-death rate imbalance is redressed by a rise in the death rate rather than by a lowering of the birth rate. Make no mistake about it, *the imbalance will be redressed.* The shape of the population growth curve is one familiar to the biologist. It is the outbreak part of an outbreak-crash sequence. A population grows rapidly in the presence of abundant resources, finally runs out of food or some other necessity, and crashes to a low level or extinction. Man is not only running out of food, he is also destroying the life support systems of the Spaceship Earth. The situation was recently summarized very succinctly: "It is the top of the ninth inning. Man, always a threat at the plate, has been hitting nature hard. It is important to remember, however, that NATURE BATS LAST."

For Discussion and Review

1. What factors brought about the failure of the "Green Revolution"? Do you believe that the "Revolution" and its failure could come about as described? Why or why not?
2. Although Ehrlich is extremely critical of man's folly, he does offer the hope that we could avoid an eco-catastrophe. What constructive suggestions can be inferred from his article?
3. Discuss the irony in Ehrlich's account of the population control bill passed in 1974. Compare your own attitude on population control to that of Ehrlich.
4. Many people believe that overpopulation is more of a problem in underdeveloped countries than in the United States. How does the "25 Indians and a dog" speech refute this belief?

Overpopulated America

BY WAYNE H. DAVIS

I define as most seriously overpopulated that nation whose people by virtue of their numbers and activities are most rapidly decreasing the ability of the land to support human life. With our large population, our affluence and our technological monstrosities, the United States wins first place by a substantial margin.

Let's compare the US to India, for example. We have 203 million people, whereas she has 540 million on much less land. But look at the impact of people on the land.

The average Indian eats his daily few cups of rice (or perhaps wheat, whose production on American farms contributed to our one percent per year drain in quality of our active farmland), draws his bucket of water from the communal well and sleeps in a mud hut. In his daily rounds to gather cow dung to burn to cook his rice and warm his feet, his footsteps, along with those of millions of his countrymen, help bring about a slow deterioration of the ability of the land to support people. His contribution to the destruction of the land is minimal.

An American, on the other hand, can be expected to destroy a piece of land on which he builds a home, garage and driveway. He will contribute his share to the 142 million tons of smoke and fumes, seven million junked cars, 20 million tons of paper, 48 billion cans, and 26 billion bottles the overburdened environment must absorb each year. To run his air conditioner we will strip-mine a Kentucky hillside, push

Wayne H. Davis, Professor of Zoology at the University of Kentucky, is the author of a nationally syndicated series of newspaper articles on "Man and Environment." He is also coauthor with Roger W. Barbour of *The Bats of America*.

Wayne H. Davis, "Overpopulated America," *The New Republic*, January 10, 1970, pp. 13–15. Reprinted by permission of the author.

the dirt and slate down into the stream, and burn coal in a power generator, whose smokestack contributes to a plume of smoke massive enough to cause cloud seeding and premature precipitation from Gulf winds which should be irrigating the wheat farms of Minnesota.

In his lifetime he will personally pollute three million gallons of water, and industry and agriculture will use ten times this much water in his behalf. To provide these needs the US Army Corps of Engineers will build dams and flood farmland. He will also use 21,000 gallons of leaded gasoline containing boron, drink 28,000 pounds of milk and eat 10,000 pounds of meat. The latter is produced and squandered in a life pattern unknown to Asians. A steer on a Western range eats plants containing minerals necessary for plant life. Some of these are incorporated into the body of the steer which is later shipped for slaughter. After being eaten by man these nutrients are flushed down the toilet into the ocean or buried in the cemetery, the surface of which is cluttered with boulders called tombstones and has been removed from productivity. The result is a continual drain on the productivity of range land. Add to this the erosion of overgrazed lands, and the effects of the falling water table as we mine Pleistocene deposits of groundwater to irrigate to produce food for more people, and we can see why our land is dying far more rapidly than did the great civilizations of the Middle East, which experienced the same cycle. The average Indian citizen, whose fecal material goes back to the land, has but a minute fraction of the destructive effect on the land that the affluent American does.

Thus, I want to introduce a new term, which I suggest be used in future discussions of human population and ecology. We should speak of our numbers in "Indian equivalents". An Indian equivalent I define as the average number of Indians required to have the same detrimental effect on the land's ability to support human life as would the average American. This value is difficult to determine, but let's take an extremely conservative working figure of 25. To see how conservative this is, imagine the addition of 1000 citizens to your town and 25,000 to an Indian village. Not only would the Americans destroy much more land for homes, highways and a shopping center, but they would contribute far more to environmental deterioration in hundreds of other ways as well. For example, their demand for steel for new autos might increase the daily pollution equivalent of 130,000 junk autos which *Life* tells us that US Steel Corp. dumps into Lake Michigan. Their demand for textiles would help the cotton industry destroy the life in the Black Warrior River in Alabama with endrin. And they would contribute to the massive industrial pollution of our oceans (we provide one third to one half the world's share) which has caused the precipitous downward trend in our commercial fisheries landings during the past seven years.

The per capita gross national product of the United States is 38 times that of India. Most of our goods and services contribute to the decline in the ability of the environment to support life. Thus it is clear that a figure of 25 for an Indian equivalent is conservative. It has been suggested to me that a more realistic figure would be 500.

In Indian equivalents, therefore, the population of the United States is at least four billion. And the rate of growth is even more alarming. We are growing at one percent per year, a rate which would double our numbers in 70 years. India is growing at 2.5 percent. Using the Indian equivalent of 25, our population growth becomes 10 times as serious as that of India. According to the Reinows in their recent book *Moment in the Sun,* just one year's crop of American babies can be expected to use up 25 billion pounds of beef, 200 million pounds of steel and 9.1 billion gallons of gasoline during their collective lifetime. And the demands on water and land for our growing population are expected to be far greater than the supply available in the year 2000. We are destroying our land at a rate of over a million acres a year. We now have only 2.6 agricultural acres per person. By 1975 this will be cut to 2.2, the critical point for the maintenance of what we consider a decent diet, and by the year 2000 we might expect to have 1.2.

You might object that I am playing with statistics in using the Indian equivalent on the rate of growth. I am making the assumption that today's Indian child will live 35 years (the average Indian life span) at today's level of influence. If he lives an American 70 years, our rate of population growth would be 20 times as serious as India's.

But the assumption of continued affluence at today's level is unfounded. If our numbers continue to rise, our standard of living will fall so sharply that by the years 2000 any surviving Americans might consider today's average Asian to be well off. Our children's destructive effects on their environment will decline as they sink lower into poverty.

The United States is in serious economic trouble now. Nothing could be more misleading than today's affluence, which rests precariously on a crumbling foundation. Our productivity, which had been increasing steadily at about 3.2 percent a year since World War II, has been falling during 1969. Our export over import balance has been shrinking steadily from $7.1 billion in 1964 to $1.05 billion in the first half of 1969. Our balance of payments deficit for the second quarter was $3.7 billion, the largest in history. We are now importing iron ore, steel, oil, beef, textiles, cameras, radios and hundreds of other things.

Our economy is based upon the Keynesian concept of a continued growth in population and productivity. It worked in an underpopulated nation with excess resources. It could continue to work only if the earth and its resources were expanding at an annual rate of 4 to

5 percent. Yet neither the number of cars, the economy, the human population, nor anything else can expand indefinitely at an exponential rate in a finite world. We must face this fact *now*. The crisis is here. When Walter Heller says that our economy will expand by 4 percent annually through the latter 1970s he is dreaming. He is in a theoretical world totally unaware of the realities of human ecology. If the economists do not wake up and devise a new system for us now somebody else will have to do it for them.

A civilization is comparable to a living organism. Its longevity is a function of its metabolism. The higher the metabolism (affluence), the shorter the life. Keynesian economics has allowed us an affluent but shortened life span. We have now run our course.

The tragedy facing the United States is even greater and more imminent than that descending upon the hungry nations. The Paddock brothers in their book, *Famine 1975!,* say that India "cannot be saved" no matter how much food we ship her. But India will be here after the United States is gone. Many millions will die in the most colossal famines India has ever known, but the land will survive and she will come back as she always has before. The United States, on the other hand, will be a desolate tangle of concrete and ticky-tacky, of strip-mined moonscape and silt-choked reservoirs. The land and water will be so contaminated with pesticides, herbicides, mercury fungicides, lead, baron, nickel, arsenic and hundreds of other toxic substances, which have been approaching critical levels of concentration in our environment as a result of our numbers and affluence, that it may be unable to sustain human life.

Thus as the curtain gets ready to fall on man's civilization let it come as no surprise that it shall first fall on the United States. And let no one make the mistake of thinking we can save ourselves by "cleaning up the environment." Banning DDT is the equivalent of the physician's treating syphilis by putting a bandaid over the first chancre to appear. In either case you can be sure that more serious and widespread trouble will soon appear unless the disease itself is treated. We cannot survive by planning to treat the symptoms such as air pollution, water pollution, soil erosion, etc.

What can we do to slow the rate of destruction of the United States as a land capable of supporting human life? There are two approaches. First, we must reverse the population growth. We have far more people than we can continue to support at anything near today's level of affluence. American women average slightly over three children each. According to the *Population Bulletin* if we reduced this number to 2.5 there would still be 330 million people in the nation at the end of the century. And even if we reduced this to 1.5 we would have 57 million more people in the year 2000 than we have now. With our present longevity patterns it would take more than 30 years for the population to peak even when reproducing at this rate, which would eventually give us a net decrease in numbers.

Do not make the mistake of thinking that technology will solve our population problem by producing a better contraceptive. Our problem now is that people want too many children. Surveys show the average number of children wanted by the American family is 3.3. There is little difference between the poor and the wealthy, black and white, Catholic and Protestant. Production of children at this rate during the next 30 years would be so catastrophic in effect on our resources and the viability of the nation as to be beyond my ability to contemplate. To prevent this trend we must not only make contraceptives and abortion readily available to everyone, but we must establish a system to put severe economic pressure on those who produce children and reward those who do not. This can be done within our system of taxes and welfare.

The other thing we must do is to pare down our Indian equivalents. Individuals in American society vary tremendously in Indian equivalents. If we plot Indian equivalents versus their reciprocal, the percentage of land surviving a generation, we obtain a linear regression. We can then place individuals and occupation types on this graph. At one end would be the starving blacks of Mississippi; they would approach unity in Indian equivalents, and would have the least destructive effect on the land. At the other end of the graph would be the politicians slicing pork for the barrel, the highway contractors, strip-mine operators, real estate developers, and public enemy number one—the US Army Corps of Engineers.

We must halt land destruction. We must abandon the view of land and minerals as private property to be exploited in any way economically feasible for private financial gain. Land and minerals are resources upon which the very survival of the nation depends, and their use must be planned in the best interests of the people.

Rising expectations for the poor is a cruel joke foisted upon them by the Establishment. As our new economy of use-it-once-and-throw-it-away produces more and more products for the affluent, the share of our resources available for the poor declines. Blessed be the starving blacks of Mississippi with their outdoor privies, for they are ecologically sound, and they shall inherit a nation. Although I hope that we will help these unfortunate people attain a decent standard of living by diverting war efforts to fertility control and job training, our most urgent task to assure this nation's survival during the next decade is to stop the affluent destroyers.

For Discussion and Review

1. How does Davis define *overpopulation?* How does his definition violate American stereotypes of countries like China and India?
2. What is an Indian equivalent? Discuss whether or not you accept 25 as a reasonably accurate Indian equivalent for the average American.
3. Why does Davis figure that our population growth is *ten times* more serious than India's?
4. Is Davis fair in using 1969 figures to predict the economic failure of the United States? Why or why not?
5. Explain how the ideas in Davis' last paragraph violate our whole approach to governmental economic planning.

Overpopulation As a Crisis Issue: The Nonsense Explosion

BY BEN WATTENBERG

As the concern about the environment has swept across the nation, the ghost of the "population explosion"—recently haunting only India and other ugly foreign places—has suddenly been domestically resurrected and we are again hearing how crowded it is in America.

Life magazine, for example, chose to launch the new decade with the headline "Squeezing into the '70s," announcing that, because of the crowds, "the despair of yesterday's soup line has been replaced by to-day's ordeal of the steak line." Two months later *Life* featured a story about a young New Jersey mathematician who had himself sterilized because he is "deeply worried by this country's wildly expanding population."

Crowded, crowded, crowded, we are told. Slums are crowded, suburbs are crowded, megalopolis is crowded and more and more people are eating up, burning up and using up the beauty and wealth of America—turning the land into a polluted, depleted sprawl of scummy water and flickering neon, an ecological catastrophe stretching from the Everglades to the Pacific Northwest. Crisis. Crisis. Crisis.

That so very much of this is preposterous, as we shall see, should come as no real surprise to those who follow the fad of crisis in America. There are no plain and simple problems any more. From poverty to race to crime to Vietnam all we face are crises which threaten to bring down the world upon our heads. And now it is ecology/environ-

---

Ben Wattenberg, who coauthored *The Real Majority* in 1970 with Richard Scammon, is probably best known as a political analyst. His earlier works include *The New Nations of Africa* with Ralph Lee Smith and *This U.S.A.* with Richard Scammon. He also served on President Johnson's White House staff.

Ben Wattenberg, "Overpopulation As a Crisis Issue: The Nonsense Explosion," *The New Republic,* April 4, 1970, pp. 18–23. Copyright 1970 by Ben Wattenberg. Reprinted by permission of the Harold Matson Company, Inc.

ment—which is a perfectly good problem to be sure—but with its advent comes dragged in by the heels our old friend the super-crisis of the population explosion, which is not nearly as real or immediate a problem in America, and ends up serving unfortunately as a political smokescreen that can obscure a host of legitimate concerns.

While the rhetoric rattles on about where will we ever put the next hundred million Americans, while the President tells us that the roots of so many of our current problems are to be found in the speed with which the last hundred million Americans came upon us, while the more apocalyptic demographers and biologists (like Dr. Paul Ehrlich) are talking about putting still nonexistent birth control chemicals in the water supply, and about federal licensing of babies—the critical facts in the argument remain generally unstated and the critical premises in the argument remain largely unchallenged.

—The critical facts are that America is not by any standard a crowded country and that the American birth rate has recently been at an all-time low.

—The critical premise is that population growth in America is harmful.

In not stating the facts and in not at least challenging the premises, politicians and planners alike seem to be leaving themselves open to both bad planning and bad politics. This happens by concentrating on what the problem is not, rather than on what the problem is. Let's then, first look at the facts. The current population of the United States is 205 million. That population is distributed over 3,615,123 square miles of land, for a density of about 55 persons per square mile. In terms of density, this makes the United States one of the most sparsely populated nations in the world. As measured by density, Holland is about 18 times as "crowded" (at 975 persons per square mile), England is 10 times as dense (588 persons per square mile), scenic Switzerland seven times as dense (382), tropical Nigeria three times as dense (174) and even neighboring Mexico beats us out with 60 persons per square mile. The US, by international standards, is not a very "crowded" country.

But density in some cases can be very misleading in trying to judge "crowdedness." The Soviet Union, for example, is less dense than the US (29 per square mile), but has millions of square miles of uninhabitable land, just as does Brazil and Australia, two other nations also less densely populated than the US.

Of course, the US also has large areas of land that are equally uninhabitable: the Rockies, the Western deserts, parts of Alaska and so on.

But while it is of interest to know that America has some land that is uninhabitable, what is of far more importance is that we have in the United States vast areas of eminently habitable land, land that in fact was inhabited until very recently. In the last eight years one out of three counties in America actually *lost* population. Four states have lost population: North and South Dakota, West Virginia, and Wyoming; and another two states, Maine and Iowa, gained less than one percent in the eight years. Furthermore, three out of five counties had a net out-migration, that is, more people left the county than came in.

These counties, the net-loss counties and the net-out-migration counties, are the areas in America where the current hoopla about the population sounds a bit hollow. These are the areas, mostly rural and small town, that are trying to attract industry, areas where a smokestack or a traffic jam signifies not pollution but progress, areas that have more open space around them for hunting and fishing than before, and areas where the older people are a little sad because, as they tell you, "the young people don't stay around here anymore."

This human plaint tells us what has been happening demographically in the United States in recent years. It has not been a population explosion, but a population redistribution. And the place people have been redistributing themselves *to* is a place we call "suburb":

AMERICAN POPULATION BY RESIDENCE

	Population		Increase
	1950	1968	1950-1968
Residing in central city	35%	29%	6 million
Residing in suburb	24%	35%	32 million (!)
Residing in small cities, towns and rural	41%	36%	9 million
	100%	100%	47 million

In less than two decades the proportion of Americans living in suburbs has gone from less than a quarter to more than a third.

But even the total increase in population—rural, city, and suburb—is misleading, The big gains in population occurred ten and fifteen years ago; today growth is much slower. Thus, in calendar year 1956, the US population grew by 3.1 million, while in calendar year 1968 population went up by 2.0 million—and in a nation with a larger population base.

What has happened, simply, is that the baby-boom has ended. When the GIs came home after World War II, they began begetting large quantities of children, and Americans went on begetting at high rates for about 15 years. The best index of population growth in the US is the fertility rate, that is, the number of babies born per thousand women aged 15–44. In 1940, the fertility rate was 80, just a few points above the 1936 Depression all-time low of 76. Ten years later, in 1950, the baby-boom had begun and the fertility rate had soared to 106, an increase of 32 percent in just ten years. It kept climbing. In 1957, it reached 123, up more than 50 percent in two decades.

But since 1957, the rate has gone steadily down: to 119 in 1960, to 98 in 1965, to 85.7 in 1968, not very much higher now than in Depression times. The estimated fertility rate for 1969 was down slightly to 85.5 and there is no reason now to think it will go up, although, as we shall see, it may sink further.

When measured by another yardstick, the "percent national population growth" (birth plus immigration less deaths), the American population is now growing by only 1.0 percent per year; just a decade ago it was growing by 1.8 percent per year. That may not sound like much of a difference, .8 percent, but in a nation of 200 million people it means 16 million fewer people over a single decade!

With all this, however, comes another important set of facts: our population *is* still growing. At the reduced growth rate there are now about two million people being added to our population each year. This may even go up somewhat in the next few years as the baby-boom babies become young adults and—roughly simultaneously—parents. Moreover, a growing population, even a slowly growing population, grows by larger numbers as it grows. As the two hundred million Americans become two hundred and fifty million Americans there is a proportionately greater number of potential mothers, more babies, and the incremental two million new Americans per year can rise to 2½ or 3 million new Americans even with a relatively low growth *rate*.

The current, most likely projection of the Census Bureau of the US population in the year 2000—three decades hence—hovers somewhere in the 280–290 million range. That means there will be about 75–85 million more Americans than today, which is many millions more indeed, although not quite the round "hundred million" figure everyone is talking about.

It must be stressed, however, that this is only a projection: it could be high, it could be low. The figure is derived from a series of four alternate projections based on different levels of fertility rates issued by the Census Bureau in 1967. Already the highest two projections—calling for 361 million and 336 million—are out of the question. The third projection called for 308 million and that too now seems high, as it called for a fertility rate of 95 in 1970—about 10 points higher than the 1969 rate. The lowest of the four projections calls for a fertility rate of 84.6 in 1970 (roughly where we are) and yields a population of 283 million in the year 2000.

But even that is not an immutable figure by any means. Just as the first of three of the alternate projections quickly proved themselves false, so it may be that Series D may prove high. After all, the Hoover

Depression, in an era with far less effective birth control technology, brought fertility rates down to 76. What might a Nixon Recession do in an era of pills, loops, diaphragms, liberalized abortion? Already the Census Bureau—quite properly—is preparing to revise its projections for the future. The new set of alternate projections—which will bracket the newer, lower, fertility rates—will unquestionably be lower, with a low-end possibly in the general area of 265 million for the year 2000. That too will only be a projection, based on assumptions which may or may not prove valid. But if such a low fertility rate does indeed occur, population in the US would then begin to level off after the year 2000 as the last of the baby-boom babies have completed their own families. The US might then be in an era of near-stable population along the lines of many Western European nations.

But even that is sixty million more Americans in just three decades—more than the population of Great Britain today.

Those, then, would seem to be the elementary facts. More Americans, although probably not as many as we may have been led to believe. More Americans, but not necessarily inhabiting a statistically crowded country.

With these facts, we can now turn to the premise set forth by the Explosionists i.e., more Americans are bad.

Are they? My own judgment is—not necessarily.

There are a number of points made by the Explosionists and they can only be briefly examined here.

Because population growth is currently being linked to environmental problems, we can look there first. The Explosionists say people, and the industry needed to support people, causes pollution. Ergo: fewer people—less pollution.

On the surface, a reasonable enough statement; certainly, population is one of the variables in the pollution problem. Yet, there is something else to be said. People not only cause pollution, but once you have a substantial number of people, it is only people that can solve pollution. Further, the case can be made that *more people* can more easily and more quickly solve pollution problems than can fewer people. For example: let us assume that $60 billion per year are necessary for national defense. The cost of defense will not necessarily be higher for a nation of three hundred million than for a nation of two hundred million. Yet the tax revenues to the government would be immensely higher, freeing vast sums of tax money to be used for the very expensive programs that are necessary for air, water, and pollution control. Spreading constant defense costs over a large population base provides proportionately greater amounts for nondefense spending. The same sort of equation can be used for the huge, one-time capital costs of research that must go into any effective, long-range anti-pollution program. The costs are roughly the same for 200 or 300 million people—but easier to pay by 300 million.

Lake Erie, the Hudson River, the Potomac, are ecological slums today. If the US population did not grow by one person over the current 205 million Americans, these bodies of waters would *still* be ecological slums. These waters, and any others now threatened, will be decent places only if men are willing to devote resources to the job. That is not a function of population growth, but of national will. It can be done if we, as a nation, decide that we want it done and are willing to pay for it. It is as simple as that and it has relatively little to do with whether the national decision involves 200 or 250 or 300 or 350 million Americans. It should also be remembered that pollution occurs in underpopulated places as well: in Sidney, Australia today, in medieval Europe, in ancient Rome.

Next, the Explosionists view more people as a crisis because of all the demands they will make upon the society. So many new schools, so many more hospitals, more libraries—services and facilities which we are having difficulty providing right now. Similarly with "new towns." If we are to avoid vast and sprawling megalopolitan swaths, we are told, we must build 100 brand-new towns in 30 years. Unfortunately, we've only been able to construct a few in the last couple of decades—so, alas, what possible chance do we have to make the grade in the years to come?

What this argument ignores, of course, is that it is not governments who really create schools, hospitals, libraries and even new towns. It is *people* who create and build. People pay taxes; the taxes build and staff the schools; the more people, the more need for schools, *and* the more taxes. In an uncanny way it usually works out that every child in America has his own set of parents, and a school to attend. In a nation of a hundred million there were roughly enough schools for the children then present, at two hundred million the same was true and, no doubt, it will hold true at three hundred million. Nor will quality suffer because of numbers; quality sufferers if taxpayers aren't willing to pay for quality and it is not harder for 300 million Americans to pay for quality schools for their children than it is for 230 million to buy quality schooling for their offspring.

And those "new towns"? *People* make them too. That's just what's been happening in America in the last few decades. We call them "suburbs," not "new towns," and as the earlier data showed, 32 million Americans opted for this "decentralization" over the past eighteen years, long before it became a fashionable, political fad-word. People did this because people are not damn fools and when they had a chance to trade a rural shack or an urban tenement for a green quarter acre in suburbia, they did so, even though the faddists then were saying that suburbia was not "decentralized" (which is allegedly good), but "conformist" (which is allegedly bad). What smug town-planners like to call urban sprawl, represents uncrowded, gracious living for the former residents of city slums and the quality of such suburban life doesn't necessarily deteriorate if another new suburb rises down the road a mile.

Now, suburbs are not identical to the new town concept. The new towns, in theory, are further away from big cities, they are largely self-contained and they are designed from scratch. But, curiously, as many jobs move from the central cities, suburbs are becoming more and more self-contained; as metropolitan areas get larger, the newer suburbs *are* quite far from central cities; and there are some fascinating new start-from-scratch concepts in planning that are now materializing in suburban areas, particularly in some of the massive all-weather, multi-tiered, multi-malled shopping centers.

All this is not to denigrate new towns or the idea of population de-centralization. Far from it. The effort here is only to point out that people often act even faster than their governments in seeking their own best interests. If it is new towns near a babbling brook that Americans feel they want, if the country remains prosperous, some patriot will no doubt step forward and provide same, and even have salesmen in boiler rooms phoning you to sell same. The process is mostly organic, not planned/governmental. It works with 200 or 250 or 300 or 350 million Americans.

There is next the "resources" argument. It comes in two parts. Part one: many of our resources are finite (oil, coal, etc.); more people obviously use more resources; the fewer the people, the less the drain on the resources. Part two: we Americans are rich people; rich people use more resources; therefore, we must cut back population particularly fast, and particularly our rich population.

The resources problem is difficult to assess. A demographer now in his sixties seemed to put it in perspective. "Resources are a serious problem," he said, "We've been running out of oil ever since I was a boy."

The fact is, of course, sooner or later we *will* run out of oil; perhaps in thirty years or fifty years, or a hundred years or two hundred years. So too will we run out of all nonrenewable resoures—by definition. We will run out of oil even if population growth stops today and we will run out of oil, somewhat sooner, if population growth continues. Whether oil reserves are depleted in 2020 or 2040 or 2140 does not seem to be of critical importance; in any event a substitute fuel must be found—probably nuclear. If no adequate substitute is developed, then we (all us earthmen) will suffer somewhat regardless of numbers.

Part two, that rich people are the real menace both resource-wise and pollution-wise, has recently been particularly stressed by Dr. Jean Mayer who advises the President hunger-wise but would not seem to be fully up to date demography-wise.

For the simple fact is that wealthier people generally have far fewer children than poorer people. With current mortality rates, population stability is maintained if the typical woman has on the average 2.13 children. In a 1964 Census Bureau survey among women who had completed their child-bearing years, it was shown that families with incomes of $10,000 and over had 2.21 children, just a trifle over replacement. This compared with 3.53 children for the poorest women. Since 1964, fertility rates have gone down among young women, and it is possible that when these lower rates are ultimately reflected as "completed fertility" we may see that affluent American women of the future just barely replace their own number, if that.

In short, current population patterns show that affluent people do not cause rapid population growth. And if the entire population were entirely affluent, we certainly would not be talking about a population explosion. Further, if the entire population were affluent *and* committed to combatting pollution, we wouldn't be talking about a pollution explosion either.

What then is Dr. Mayer's prescription? Is he against affluent people having babies but not poor people, even though the affluent have relatively few anyway? Or perhaps is it that he is just against the idea of letting any more poor people become affluent people, because they too will then consume too many resources and cause more pollution?

There are two important points that run through most of the above. First is that the simple numbers of people are not in themselves of great importance in the United States. There is no "optimum" population as such for the U.S., not within population ranges now forecast in any event. Whether we have 250 million people or 350 million people is less important than what the people—however many of them there are—decide to do about their problems. Second the population problem, at least in the United States, is an extremely long-term proposition, and in a country of this size and wealth, there is more flexibility in solving the potential demographic problems than might be assumed from the current rhetoric-of-crisis.

To be sure, much of the concern about population growth is sane, valid, and important. Certainly the concept of family planning—which for years had been a political stepchild—is now coming into the mainstream, and properly so. That every family in America should at least have the knowledge and the technology to control the size of its family as it sees fit seems beyond question. This knowledge and this technology, previously available largely to middle-class and affluent Americans, is now being made available to poorer Americans through growing federal programs. Some of the more militant black leaders have called it "genocide," but that is a rather hollow charge when one realizes a) that the poorest American women now have about 50 percent more children per capita than do middle-class Americans and b) that more-children-than-can-be-properly-provided-for is one of the most classic causes of poverty in America and around the world.

Certainly too, population growth must sooner or later level off. While America could support twice its current population and probably four times its current population—growth can obviously not go on forever and it is wise to understand this fact now rather than a hundred years from now. It is also wise to begin to act upon this knowledge, as indeed we have begun to act upon it. It is, accordingly, difficult to complain about the suggestions for legislation to make conditions easier for women to get and hold decent jobs—the thought being that easier access to employment will slow the birth rate. Our problems in the future probably will be easier to handle with somewhat fewer people than with somewhat greater numbers.

But what is wrong, and dangerous, and foolhardy is to make population a crisis. Doing so will simply allow too many politicans to take their eyes off the ball. When Explosionists say, as they do, that crime, riots, and urban problems are caused by "the population explosion," it is just too easy, for politicians to agree and say sure, let's stop having so many babies, instead of saying let's get to work on the real urban problems of this nation. (As a matter of general interest it should be noted that the riot areas, the high-crime areas, the areas of the most acute urban problems are areas that are typically losing population. For example, special censuses in Hough and Watts showed population *loss*. Given that kind of data it is hard to accept the Explosionist notion that crowding causes crime.)

When the Explosionists say, as they do, that Yosemite and Yellowstone are crowded and that there is a vanishing wilderness because of too many people—they are wrong again. When visits to national parks have gone up by more than 400 percent in less than two decades, while population growth has gone up by about 30 percent, over the same time, then Yosemite isn't crowded because of population but because of other factors. When you have a nation where a workingman can afford a car, and/or a camper-trailer, when you give him three weeks paid vacation, provide decent roads—there would be something to say for the fact that you have indeed set up the society that Old Liberals, Trade Union Variety, lusted for, and who is to say that is bad? Again, if the population-crisis rhetoric is accepted it becomes too easy to say that the way to an uncrowded Yosemite is to have fewer people, and forget about the hard and far more costly problems of creating more recreation areas, which are needed even if our population does not rise.

When the Explosionists say, as they do, that it's because we have so many people that Lake Erie is polluted then once again we are invited to take our eye off the tens-of-billions-of-dollars ball of environmental safety and we are simultaneously invited to piddle around with 25-million dollar programs for birth control, which are nice, but don't solve anything to do with Lake Erie.

Finally, we must take note of the new thrust by the Explosionists: population control. Note the phrase carefully. This is specifically not "family planning," where the family concerned does the planning. This is control of population by the government and this is what the apocalyptics are demanding, because, they say, family planning by itself will not reduce us to a zero growth rate. The more popular "soft" position of government control involves what is called "disincentives," that is, a few minor measures like changing the taxation system, the school system and the moral code to see if that won't work before going onto outright baby licensing.

Accordingly, the demographer Judith Blake Davis of the University of California (Berkeley) complained to a House Committee: "We penalize homosexuals of both sexes, we insist that women must bear unwanted children by depriving them of ready access to abortion, *we bind individuals to pay for the education of other people's children, we make people with small families support the schooling of others. . . ."* (Italics mine.)

Now, Dr. Davis is not exactly saying that we should go to a private school system or eliminate the tax exemption for children thereby penalizing the poor but not the rich—but that is the implication. In essence, Senator Packwood recently proposed just that: no tax exemptions for any children beyond the second per family, born after 1972.

The strong position on population control ultimately comes around to some form of governmental permission, or licensing, for babies.

Dr. Garrett Hardin, a professor-biologist at the University of California, Santa Barbara, says "In the long run, voluntarism is insanity. The result will be continued uncontrolled population growth."

Astrophysicist Donald Aiken says, "The government has to step in and tamper with religious and personal convictions—maybe even impose penalties for every child a family has beyond two."

Dr. Melvin Ketchel, professor of physiology at Tufts Medical School writes in *Medical World News*: "Scientists will discover ways of controlling the fertility of an entire population . . . the compound . . . could be controlled by adjustments in dosage, [and] a government could regulate the growth of its population without depending upon the voluntary action of individual couples . . . such an agent might be added to the water supply."

And Dr. Paul Ehrlich of Stanford: "If we don't do something dramatic about population and environment, and do it immediately, there's just no hope that civilization will persist. . . . The world's most serious population-growth problem is right here in the United States among affluent white Americans. . . ."

What it all adds up to is this: why have a long-range manageable population problem that can be coped with gradually over generations when, with a little extra souped-up scare rhetoric, we can drum up a full-fledged crisis? We certainly need one; it's been months since we've had a crisis. After all, Vietnam, we were told, was "the greatest crisis in a hundred years." Piker. Here's a crisis that's a beauty: the greatest crisis in two billion years: we're about to breed ourselves right into oblivion.

Finally, look at it all from Mr. Nixon's point of view. It's beautiful. You (Mr. Nixon) take office and the major domestic problems, generally acknowledged, are the race situation and the (so-called) crisis of the cities. They are tough problems. They are controversial problems. They are problems that have given way only gradually, painstakingly, expensively, over the years. Your opponents are in a militant mood. They have been co-opted in Vietnam and you fully expect them to hold your feet to the fire on these tough domestic problems.

Apprehensively, you await the onslaught. And what is the slogan? No, it . . . can't be—but yes, it is. It's coming into focus. Read it: "Lower Emission Standards"! And in the next rank is another militant sign; and what does it say? It says, "Our Rivers Stink."

Full circle. The opposition sloganeers have gone from the "New Deal" to the "Fair Deal," to the "New Frontier" to the "Great Society," and now they march to a new banner: "No Shit"!

Beautiful. Of course the environment *is* a real problem, an important problem; we knew that from Senator Muskie. Of course your President will respond to it, particularly since almost everyone is for it, particularly if it takes the heat off elsewhere. But even the environment issue is massively expensive—too expensive to do everything now that ought to be done now.

So wait a minute, you say, your opponents have been good to you so far, let's see how really helpful they'll be. And behold, here comes the cavalry.

And what do they say? The problem of pollution is really the problem of too many people. Let the opponents divide among themselves and let the opponents fight among themselves. Let there be a children's allowance, say some of your opponents. Nay, let there not be a children's allowance, it will encourage population growth. Let there be better public schools, say some of your enemies. Nay, let each family pay for their own schooling to discourage population growth. Let us help the poor, say the opponents; nay, let us penalize the poor for having too many children. Let then the Secretary of HEW go forth to the people and say, "Ask not what your country can do for you, ask what you can do for your country—you shall have two children no more, no less, that is your brave social mission in America."

I imagine there have been luckier Presidents, but I can't think of any.

For Discussion and Review

1. What role does affluence play in the pollution problem? How do Wattenberg's views on affluence differ from those of Davis and Ehrlich?
2. Discuss Wattenberg's contention that there are always enough schools to support the population, assessing the quality of the schools you have attended. If you disagree with Wattenberg, what factors do you think he has failed to consider?
3. Wattenberg states that if there is a demand for a new town or suburb, one will be built. Indicate why you agree or disagree with this view.
4. Is Wattenberg's argument that the "population explosion" can become a "red herring" a valid one? Why or why not? Cite recent examples to support your opinion.

Nature Fights Back

BY RACHEL L. CARSON

To have risked so much in our efforts to mold nature to our satisfaction and yet to have failed in achieving our goal would indeed be the final irony. Yet this, it seems, is our situation. The truth, seldom mentioned but there for anyone to see, is that nature is not so easily molded and that the insects are finding ways to circumvent our chemical attacks on them.

"The insect world is nature's most astonishing phenomenon," said the Dutch biologist C. J. Briejer. "Nothing is impossible to it; the most improbable things commonly occur there. One who penetrates deeply into its mysteries is continually breathless with wonder. He knows that anything can happen, and that the completely impossible often does."

The "impossible" is now happening on two broad fronts. By a process of genetic selection, the insects are developing strains resistant to chemicals. . . . But the broader problem . . . is the fact that our chemical attack is weakening the defenses inherent in the environment itself, defenses designed to keep the various species in check. Each time we breach these defenses a horde of insects pours through.

From all over the world come reports that make it clear we are in a serious predicament. At the end of a decade or more of intensive chemical control, entomologists were finding that problems they had considered solved a few years earlier had returned to plague them. And new problems had arisen as insects once present only in insignificant

Rachel Carson, a famous biologist, was the recipient of several honorary degrees and numerous writing awards. In addition to many scientific articles, her writings include *Under the Sea Wind* and *The Edge of the Sea*. She is best known for *Silent Spring*, which has been one of the main catalysts for the current interest in ecology

Rachel Carson, "Nature Fights Back," in *Silent Spring* (Boston: Houghton Mifflin Company, 1962), pp. 245–261. Reprinted by permission.

numbers had increased to the status of serious pests. By their very nature chemical controls are self-defeating, for they have been devised and applied without taking into account the complex biological systems against which they have been blindly hurled. The chemicals may have been pretested against a few individual species, but not against living communities.

In some quarters nowadays it is fashionable to dismiss the balance of nature as a state of affairs that prevailed in an earlier, simpler world —a state that has now been so thoroughly upset that we might as well forget it. Some find this a convenient assumption, but as a chart for a course of action it is highly dangerous. The balance of nature is not the same today as in Pleistocene times, but it is still there: a complex, precise, and highly integrated system of relationships between living things which cannot safely be ignored any more than the law of gravity can be defied with impunity by man perched on the edge of a cliff. The balance of nature is not a *status quo*; it is fluid, ever shifting, in a constant state of adjustment. Man, too, is part of this balance. Sometimes the balance is in his favor; sometimes—and all too often through his own activities—it is shifted to his disadvantage.

Two critically important facts have been overlooked in designing the modern insect control programs. The first is that the really effective control of insects is that applied by nature, not by man. Populations are kept in check by something the ecologists call the resistance of the environment, and this has been so since the first life was created. The amount of food available, conditions of weather and climate, the presence of competing or predatory species, all are critically important. "The greatest single factor in preventing insects from overwhelming the rest of the world is the internecine warfare which they carry out among themselves," said the entomologist Robert Metcalf. Yet most of the chemicals now used kill all insects, our friends and enemies alike.

The second neglected fact is the truly explosive power of a species to reproduce once the resistance of the environment has been weakened. The fecundity of many forms of life is almost beyond our power to imagine, though now and then we have suggestive glimpses. I remember from student days the miracle that could be wrought in a jar containing a simple mixture of hay and water merely by adding to it a few drops of material from a mature culture of protozoa. Within a few days the jar would contain a whole galaxy of whirling, darting life—uncountable trillions of the slipper animalcule, *Paramecium*, each small as a dust grain, all multiplying without restraint in their temporary Eden of favorable temperatures, abundant food, absence of enemies. Or I think of shore rocks white with barnacles as far as the eye can see, or of the spectacle of passing through an immense school of jellyfish, mile after mile, with seemingly no end to the pulsing, ghostly forms scarcely more substantial than the water itself.

We see the miracle of nature's control at work when the cod move through winter seas to their spawning grounds, where each female deposits several millions of eggs. The sea does not become a solid mass of cod as it would surely do if all the progeny of all the cod were to survive. The checks that exist in nature are such that out of the millions of young produced by each pair only enough, on the average, survive to adulthood to replace the parent fish.

Biologists used to entertain themselves by speculating as to what would happen if, through some unthinkable catastrophe, the natural restraints were thrown off and all the progeny of a single individual survived. Thus Thomas Huxley a century ago calculated that a single female aphis (which has the curious power of reproducing without mating) could produce progeny in a single year's time whose total weight would equal that of the inhabitants of the Chinese empire of his day.

Fortunately for us such an extreme situation is only theoretical, but the dire results of upsetting nature's own arrangements are well known to students of animal populations. The stockman's zeal for eliminating the coyote has resulted in plagues of field mice, which the coyote formerly controlled. The oft repeated story of the Kaibab deer in Arizona is another case in point. At one time the deer population was in equilibrium with its environment. A number of predators—wolves, pumas, and coyotes—prevented the deer from outrunning their food supply. Then a campaign was begun to "conserve" the deer by killing off their enemies. Once the predators were gone, the deer increased prodigiously and soon there was not enough food for them. The browse line on the trees went higher and higher as they sought food, and in time many more deer were dying of starvation than had formerly been killed by predators. The whole environment, moreover, was damaged by their desperate efforts to find food.

The predatory insects of field and forests play the same role as the wolves and coyotes of the Kaibab. Kill them off and the population of the prey insect surges upward.

No one knows how many species of insects inhabit the earth because so many are yet to be identified. But more than 700,000 have already been described. This means that in terms of the number of species, 70 to 80 per cent of the earth's creatures are insects. The vast majority of these insects are held in check by natural forces, without any intervention by man. If this were not so, it is doubtful that any conceivable volume of chemicals—or any other methods—could possibly keep down their populations.

The trouble is that we are seldom aware of the protection afforded by natural enemies until it fails. Most of us walk unseeing through the world, unaware alike of its beauties, its wonders, and the strange and sometimes terrible intensity of the lives that are being lived about us. So it is that the activities of the insect predators and parasites are known to few. Perhaps we may have noticed an oddly shaped insect of ferocious mien on a bush in the garden and been dimly aware that the praying mantis lives at the expense of other insects. But we see with understanding eye only if we have walked in the garden at night and here and there with a flashlight have glimpsed the mantis stealthily creeping upon her prey. Then we sense something of the drama of the hunter and the hunted. Then we begin to feel something of that relentlessly pressing force by which nature controls her own.

The predators—insects that kill and consume other insects—are of many kinds. Some are quick and with the speed of swallows snatch their prey from the air. Others plod methodically along a stem, plucking off and devouring sedentary insects like the aphids. The yellowjackets capture soft-bodied insects and feed the juices to their young. Muddauber wasps build columned nests of mud under the eaves of houses and stock them with insects on which their young will feed. The horseguard wasp hovers above herds of grazing cattle, destroying the blood-sucking flies that torment them. The loudly buzzing syrphid fly, often mistaken for a bee, lays its eggs on leaves of aphis-infested plants; the hatching larvae then consume immense numbers of aphids. Ladybugs or lady beetles are among the most effective destroyers of aphids, scale insects, and other plant-eating insects. Literally hundreds of aphids are consumed by a single ladybug to stoke the little fires of energy which she requires to produce even a single batch of eggs.

Even more extraordinary in their habits are the parasitic insects. These do not kill their hosts outright. Instead, by a variety of adaptations they utilize their victims for the nurture of their own young. They may deposit their eggs within the larvae or eggs of their prey, so that their own developing young may find food by consuming the host. Some attach their eggs to a caterpillar by means of a sticky solution; on hatching, the larval parasite bores through the skin of the host. Others, led by an instinct that simulates foresight, merely lay their eggs on a leaf so that a browsing caterpillar will eat them inadvertently.

Everywhere, in field and hedgerow and garden and forest, the insect predators and parasites are at work. Here, above a pond, the dragonflies dart and the sun strikes fire from their wings. So their ancestors sped through swamps where huge reptiles lived. Now, as in those ancient times, the sharp-eyed dragonflies capture mosquitoes in the air, scooping them in with basket-shaped legs. In the waters below, their young, the dragonfly nymphs, or naiads, prey on the aquatic stages of mosquitoes and other insects.

Or there, almost invisible against a leaf, is the lacewing, with green gauze wings and golden eyes, shy and secretive, descendant of an ancient race that lived in Permian times. The adult lacewing feeds mostly on plant nectars and the honeydew of aphids, and in time she lays her eggs, each on the end of a long stalk which she fastens to a leaf. From these emerge her children—strange, bristled larvae called aphis lions, which live by preying on aphids, scales, or mites, which they capture and suck dry of fluid. Each may consume several hundred aphids before the ceaseless turning of the cycle of its life brings the time when it will spin a white silken cocoon in which to pass the pupal stage.

And there are many wasps, and flies as well, whose very existence depends on the destruction of the eggs or larvae of other insects through parasitism. Some of the egg parasites are exceedingly minute wasps, yet by their numbers and their great activity they hold down the abundance of many crop-destroying species.

All these small creatures are working—working in sun and rain, during the hours of darkness, even when winter's grip has damped down the fires of life to mere embers. Then this vital force is merely smoldering, awaiting the time to flare again into activity when spring awakens the insect world. Meanwhile, under the white blanket of snow, below the frost-hardened soil, in crevices in the bark of trees, and in sheltered caves, the parasites and the predators have found ways to tide themselves over the season of cold.

The eggs of the mantis are secure in little cases of thin parchment attached to the branch of a shrub by the mother who lived her life span with the summer that is gone.

The female *Polistes* wasp, taking shelter in a forgotten corner of some atttic, carries in her body the fertilized eggs, the heritage on which the whole future of her colony depends. She, the lone survivor, will start a small paper nest in the spring, lay a few eggs in its cells, and carefully rear a small force of workers. With their help she will then enlarge the nest and develop the colony. Then the workers, foraging ceaselessly through the hot days of summer, will destroy countless caterpillars.

Thus, through the circumstances of their lives, and the nature of our own wants, all these have been our allies in keeping the balance of nature tilted in our favor. Yet we have turned our artillery against our friends. The terrible danger is that we have grossly underestimated their value in keeping at bay a dark tide of enemies that, without their help, can overrun us.

The prospect of a general and permanent lowering of environmental resistance becomes grimly and increasingly real with each passing year as the number, variety, and destructiveness of insecticides grows. With the passage of time we may expect progressively more serious outbreaks of insects, both disease-carrying and crop-destroying species, in excess of anything we have ever known.

"Yes, but isn't this all theoretical?" you may ask. "Surely it won't really happen—not in my lifetime, anyway."

But it is happening, here and now. Scientific journals had already recorded some 50 species involved in violent dislocations of nature's balance by 1958. More examples are being found every year. A recent review of the subject contained references to 215 papers reporting or discussing unfavorable upsets in the balance of insect populations caused by pesticides.

Sometimes the result of chemical spraying has been a tremendous upsurge of the very insect the spraying was intended to control, as when blackflies in Ontario became 17 times more abundant after spraying than they had been before. Or when in England an enormous outbreak of the cabbage aphid—an outbreak that had no parallel on record—followed spraying with one of the organic phosphorus chemicals.

At other times spraying, while reasonably effective against the target insect, has let loose a whole Pandora's box of destructive pests that had never previously been abundant enough to cause trouble. The spider mite, for example, has become practically a worldwide pest as DDT and other insecticides have killed off its enemies. The spider mite is not an insect. It is a barely visible eight-legged creature belonging to the group that includes spiders, scorpions, and ticks. It has mouth parts adapted for piercing and sucking, and a prodigious appetite for the chlorophyll that makes the world green. It inserts these minute and stiletto-sharp mouth parts into the outer cells of leaves and evergreen needles and extracts the chlorophyll. A mild infestation gives trees and shrubbery a mottled or salt-and-pepper appearance; with a heavy mite population, foliage turns yellow and falls.

This is what happened in some of the western national forests a few years ago, when in 1956 the United States Forest Service sprayed some 885,000 acres of forested lands with DDT. The intention was to control the spruce budworm, but the following summer it was discovered that a problem worse than the budworm damage had been created. In surveying the forests from the air, vast blighted areas could be seen where the magnificent Douglas firs were turning brown and dropping their needles. In the Helena National Forest and on the western slopes of the Big Belt Mountains, then in other areas of Montana and down into Idaho the forests looked as though they had been scorched. It was evident that this summer of 1957 had brought the most extensive and spectacular infestation of spider mites in history. Almost all of the sprayed area was affected. Nowhere else was the damage evident. Searching for precedents, the foresters could remember other scourges of spider mites, though less dramatic than this one. There had been similar trouble along the Madison River in Yellowstone Park in 1929, in Colorado 20 years later, and then in New Mexico in 1956. *Each of these outbreaks had followed forest spraying with insecticides.* (The 1929 spraying, occurring before the DDT era, employed lead arsenate.)

Why does the spider mite appear to thrive on insecticides? Besides the obvious fact that it is relatively insensitive to them, there seem to be two other reasons. In nature it is kept in check by various predators such as ladybugs, a gall midge, predaceous mites and several pirate bugs, all of them extremely sensitive to insecticides. The third reason has to do with population pressure within the spider mite colonies. An undisturbed colony of mites is a densely settled community, huddled under a protective webbing for concealment from its enemies. When sprayed, the colonies disperse as the mites, irritated though not killed by the chemicals, scatter out in search of places where they will not be disturbed. In so doing they find a far greater abundance of space and food than was available in the former colonies. Their enemies are now dead so there is no need for the mites to spend their energy in secreting protective webbing. Instead, they pour all their energies into producing more mites. It is not uncommon for their egg production to be increased threefold—all through the beneficent effect of insecticides.

In the Shenandoah Valley of Virginia, a famous apple-growing region, hordes of a small insect called the red-banded leaf roller arose to plague the growers as soon as DDT began to replace arsenate of lead. Its depredations had never before been important; soon its toll rose to 50 per cent of the crop and it achieved the status of the most destructive pest of apples, not only in this region but throughout much of the East and Midwest, as the use of DDT increased.

The situation abounds in ironies. In the apple orchards of Nova Scotia in the late 1940's the worst infestations of the codling moth (cause of "wormy apples") were in the orchards regularly sprayed. In unsprayed orchards the moths were not abundant enough to cause real trouble.

Diligence in spraying had a similarly unsatisfactory reward in the eastern Sudan, where cotton growers had a bitter experience with DDT. Some 60,000 acres of cotton were being grown under irrigation in the Gash Delta. Early trials of DDT having given apparently good results, spraying was intensified. It was then that trouble began. One of the most destructive enemies of cotton is the bollworm. But the more cotton was sprayed, the more bollworms appeared. The unsprayed cotton suffered less damage to fruits and later to mature bolls than the sprayed, and in twice-sprayed fields the yield of seed cotton dropped significantly. Although some of the leaf-feeding insects were eliminated, any benefit that might thus have been gained was more than offset by bollworm damage. In the end the growers were faced with the unpleasant truth that their cotton yield would have been greater had they saved themselves the trouble and expense of spraying.

In the Belgian Congo and Uganda the results of heavy applications of DDT against an insect pest of the coffee bush were almost "catastrophic." The pest itself was found to be almost completely unaffected by the DDT, while its predator was extremely sensitive.

In America, farmers have repeatedly traded one insect enemy for a worse one as spraying upsets the population dynamics of the insect world. Two of the mass-spraying programs recently carried out have had precisely this effect. One was the fire ant eradication program in the South; the other was the spraying for the Japanese beetle in the Midwest.

When a wholesale application of heptachlor was made to the farmlands in Louisiana in 1957, the result was the unleashing of one of the worst enemies of the sugarcane crop—the sugarcane borer. Soon after the heptachlor treatment, damage by borers increased sharply. The chemical aimed at the fire ant had killed off the enemies of the borer. The crop was so severely damaged that farmers sought to bring suit against the state for negligence in not warning them that this might happen.

The same bitter lesson was learned by Illinois farmers. After the devastating bath of dieldrin recently administered to the farmlands in eastern Illinois for the control of the Japanese beetle, farmers discovered that corn borers had increased enormously in the treated area. In fact, corn grown in fields within this area contained almost twice as many of the destructive larvae of this insect as did the corn grown outside. The farmers may not yet be aware of the biological basis of what has happened, but they need no scientists to tell them they have made a poor bargain. In trying to get rid of one insect, they have brought on a scourge of a much more destructive one. According to Department of Agriculture estimates, total damage by the Japanese beetle in the United States adds up to about 10 million dollars a year, while damage by the corn borer runs to about 85 million. . . .

It is worth noting that natural forces had been heavily relied on for control of the corn borer. Within two years after this insect was accidentally introduced from Europe in 1917, the United States Government had mounted one of its most intensive programs for locating and importing parasites of an insect pest. Since that time 24 species of parasites of the corn borer have been brought in from Europe and the Orient at considerable expense. Of these, 5 are recognized as being of distinct value in control. Needless to say, the results of all this work are now jeopardized as the enemies of the corn borer are killed off by the sprays.

If this seems absurd, consider the situation in the citrus groves of California, where the world's most famous and successful experiment in biological control was carried out in the 1880's. In 1872 a scale insect that feeds on the sap of citrus trees appeared in California and within the next 15 years developed into a pest so destructive that the fruit crop in many orchards was a complete loss. The young citrus industry was threatened with destruction. Many farmers gave up and pulled out their trees. Then a parasite of the scale insect was imported from Australia, a small lady beetle called the vedalia. Within only two years after the first shipment of the beetles, the scale was under complete control throughout the citrus-growing sections of California. From that time on one could search for days among the orange groves without finding a single scale insect.

Then in the 1940's the citrus growers began to experiment with glamorous new chemicals against other insects. With the advent of DDT and the even more toxic chemicals to follow, the populations of the vedalia in many sections of California were wiped out. Its importation had cost the government a mere $5000. Its activities had saved the fruit growers several millions of dollars a year, but in a moment of heedlessness the benefit was canceled out. Infestations of the scale insect quickly reappeared and damage exceeded anything that had been seen for fifty years.

"This possibly marked the end of an era," said Dr. Paul DeBach of the Citrus Experiment Station in Riverside. Now control of the scale has become enormously complicated. The vedalia can be maintained only by repeated releases and by the most careful attention to spray schedules, to minimize their contact with insecticides. And regardless of what the citrus growers do, they are more or less at the mercy of the owners of adjacent acreages, for severe damage has been done by insecticidal drift.

All these examples concern insects that attack agricultural crops. What of those that carry disease? There have already been warnings. On Nissan Island in the South Pacific, for example, spraying had been carried on intensively during the Second World War, but was stopped when hostilities came to an end. Soon swarms of a malaria-carrying mosquito reinvaded the island. All of its predators had been killed off and there had not been time for new populations to become established. The way was therefore clear for a tremendous population explosion. Marshall Laird, who has described this incident, compares chemical control to a treadmill; once we have set foot on it we are unable to stop for fear of the consequences.

In some parts of the world disease can be linked with spraying in quite a different way. For some reason, snail-like mollusks seem to be almost immune to the effects of insecticides. This has been observed many times. In the general holocaust that followed the spraying of salt marshes in eastern Florida, aquatic snails alone survived. The scene as described was a macabre picture—something that might have been created by a surrealist brush. The snails moved among the bodies of the dead fishes and the moribund crabs, devouring the victims of the death rain of poison.

But why is this important? It is important because many aquatic snails serve as hosts of dangerous parastic worms that spend part of their life cycle in a mollusk, part in a human being. Examples are the blood flukes, or schistosoma, that cause serious disease in man when they enter the body by way of drinking water or through the skin when people are bathing in infested waters. The flukes are released into the water by the host snails. Such diseases are especially prevalent in parts of Asia and Africa. Where they occur, insect control measures that favor a vast increase of snails are likely to be followed by grave consequences.

And of course man is not alone in being subject to snail-borne disease. Liver disease in cattle, sheep, goats, deer, elk, rabbits, and various other warm-blooded animals may be caused by liver flukes that spend part of their life cycles in fresh-water snails. Livers infested with these worms are unfit for use as human food and are routinely condemned. Such rejections cost American cattlemen about 3½ million dollars annually. Anything that acts to increase the number of snails can obviously make this problem an even more serious one.

Over the past decade these problems have cast long shadows, but we have been slow to recognize them. Most of those best fitted to develop natural controls and assist in putting them into effect have been too busy laboring in the more exciting vineyards of chemical control. It was reported in 1960 that only 2 per cent of all the economic entomologists in the country were then working in the field of biological controls. A substantial number of the remaining 98 per cent were engaged in research on chemical insecticides.

Why should this be? The major chemical companies are pouring money into the universities to support research on insecticides. This creates attractive fellowships for graduate students and attractive staff positions. Biological-control studies, on the other hand, are never so endowed—for the simple reason that they do not promise anyone the fortunes that are to be made in the chemical industry. These are left to state and federal agencies, where the salaries paid are far less.

This situation also explains the otherwise mystifying fact that certain outstanding entomologists are among the leading advocates of chemical control. Inquiry into the background of some of these men reveals that their entire research program is supported by the chemical industry. Their professional prestige, sometimes their very jobs depend on the perpetuation of chemical methods. Can we then expect them to bite the hand that literally feeds them? But knowing their bias, how much credence can we give to their protests that insecticides are harmless?

Amid the general acclaim for chemicals as the principal method of insect control, minority reports have occasionally been filed by those few entomologists who have not lost sight of the fact that they are neither chemists nor engineers, but biologists.

F. H. Jacob in England has declared that "the activities of many so-called economic entomologists would make it appear that they operate in the belief that salvation lies at the end of a spray nozzle . . . that when they have created problems of resurgence or resistance or mammalian toxicity, the chemist will be ready with another pill. That view is not held here . . . Ultimately only the biologist will provide the answers to the basic problems of pest control."

"Economic entomologists must realize," wrote A. D. Pickett of Nova Scotia, "that they are dealing with living things . . . their work must be more than simply insecticide testing or a quest for highly destructive chemicals." Dr. Pickett himself was a pioneer in the field of working out sane methods of insect control that take full advantage of the predatory and parasitic species. The method which he and his associates evolved is today a shining model but one too little emulated. Only in the integrated control programs developed by some California entomologists do we find anything comparable in this country.

Dr. Pickett began his work some thirty-five years ago in the apple orchards of the Annapolis Valley in Nova Scotia, once one of the most concentrated fruit-growing areas in Canada. At that time it was believed that insecticides—then inorganic chemicals—would solve the problems of insect control, that the only task was to induce fruit growers to follow the recommended methods. But the rosy picture failed to materialize. Somehow the insects persisted. New chemicals were added, better spraying equipment was devised, and the zeal for spraying increased, but the insect problem did not get any better. Then DDT promised to "obliterate the nightmare" of codling moth outbreaks. What actually resulted from its use was an unprecedented scourge of mites. "We move from crisis to crisis, merely trading one problem for another," said Dr. Pickett.

At this point, however, Dr. Pickett and his associates struck out on a new road instead of going along with other entomologists who continued to pursue the will-o'-the-wisp of the ever more toxic chemical.

Recognizing that they had a strong ally in nature, they devised a program that makes maximum use of natural controls and minimum use of insecticides. Whenever insecticides are applied only minimum dosages are used—barely enough to control the pest without avoidable harm to beneficial species. Proper timing also enters in. Thus, if nicotine sulphate is applied before rather than after the apple blossoms turn pink one of the important predators is spared, probably because it is still in the egg stage.

Dr. Pickett uses special care to select chemicals that will do as little harm as possible to insect parasites and predators. "When we reach the point of using DDT, parathion, chlordane, and other new insecticides as routine control measures in the same way we have used the inorganic chemicals in the past, entomologists interested in biological control may as well throw in the sponge," he says. Instead of these highly toxic, broad-spectrum insecticides, he places chief reliance on ryania (derived from ground stems of a tropical plant), nicotine sulphate, and lead arsenate. In certain situations very weak concentrations of DDT or malathion are used (1 or 2 ounces per 100 gallons—in contrast to the usual 1 or 2 pounds per 100 gallons). Although these two are the least toxic of the modern insecticides, Dr. Pickett hopes by further research to replace them with safer and more selective materials.

How well has this program worked? Nova Scotia orchardists who are following Dr. Pickett's modified spray program are producing as high a proportion of first-grade fruit as are those who are using intensive chemical applications. They are also getting as good production. They are getting these results, moreover, at a substantially lower cost. The outlay for insecticides in Nova Scotia apple orchards is only from 10 to 20 per cent of the amount spent in most other apple-growing areas.

More important than even these excellent results is the fact that the modified program worked out by these Nova Scotian entomologists is not doing violence to nature's balance. It is well on the way to realizing the philosophy stated by the Canadian entomologist G. C. Ullyett a decade ago: "We must change our philosophy, abandon our attitude of human superiority and admit that in many cases in natural environments we find ways and means of limiting populations of organisms in a more economical way than we can do it ourselves."

For Discussion and Review

1. According to Rachel Carson, why are the controls of nature more effective than the controls of man in combating insects? What solutions does she suggest to replace the use of pesticides for insect control? How would these changes help the balance of nature?
2. What is the difference between a predator and a parasitic insect?
3. Explain why the infestation of insect pests is often induced by massive pesticide spraying.
4. Carson points out that we have emphasized and put much more money into research involving chemical, rather than biological, controls. How does this fact support Lynn White's argument?

DDT: It Is Needed Against Malaria, but for the Whole Environment...

BY JAMES W. WRIGHT

A quarter of a century ago Greece had two million cases of malaria a year; last year it had seven. This decrease is one measure of the largest and most successful public health program ever undertaken: worldwide eradication of malaria. Credit for our success to date belongs to the insecticide, DDT. By spraying it on the inside walls of houses, we kill the mosquitoes that carry the disease, and in doing so we do no significant harm to man or his environment.

Now, though, the supplies of this material with which we are saving lives and improving health are threatened. Because of its indiscriminate use in the past, many are demanding an equally indiscriminate worldwide ban.

Such a ban would make our program forbiddingly expensive. Although we are working on substitutes including other insecticides and biological controls, none of them is ready for large-scale use at a price that the nations in need can now afford. Legislation against manufacture and export of DDT, particularly in the United States, can bring a major international disaster: the return of malaria epidemics—suffering and debilitation from hundreds of millions of cases—deaths from tens of thousands of them.

This malaria program is the most striking of several ways in which the persistent synthetic organic insecticides have brought immense

James W. Wright is the chief of Vector Biology and Control at the World Health Organization in Geneva. As the head of a program dealing with insect disease-carriers, their genetics, and the use of pesticides as an insect deterrent, he has had first-hand experience with the subject of his article. He is also co-editor of *Genetics of Insect Vectors of Disease*.

benefits to people in almost every part of the world. During the last 25 years they have been particularly useful in developing countries of the tropics and subtropics. This group of chemicals revolutionized the whole concept of control of disease-carrying insects. For the first time in the history of public health, it was possible to contemplate the control and even eradication of some of the insect-borne diseases that have, for centuries, been insurmountable barriers to social and economic progress. Through their use, epidemics of typhus fever, yellow fever and plague are now rare, and those that do occur can be readily controlled; sleeping sickness and river blindness are being cleared from some of the most fertile areas of Africa; diseases such as relapsing fever and hemorrhagic fever are being brought under control in many countries.

In 1945, when control based on spraying of persistent materials was begun, 1.8 billion persons lived in malarious areas, the majority in rural communities. To assess the human suffering and death from this disease is almost impossible, but it has been estimated that each year malaria was contracted by 300 to 400 million persons and that it killed between three and four million of these. Losses to agricultural and industrial production are beyond measurement. In 1955 member countries of the World Health Organization (WHO) embarked on a global effort to eradicate malaria. By 1969 this had almost been achieved in areas occupied by almost 700 million people; eradication programs were being carried out in places where another 700 million lived, and help and advice on eradication were being given to governments responsible for the health of the remaining 400 million who are exposed to the disease. Almost half of the objectives set in 1955 have been achieved and strenuous efforts are directed toward the rest.

These figures become even more impressive when they are related to specific populations. For example, at the end of World War II, the two million annual cases of the disease in Greece resulted in more than 10,000 deaths. A control program was started in 1946, and within three years the number of cases reported each year had been reduced 40-fold to 50,000.

The Republic of the Philippines had 20 million people in 1951 when a survey showed that two million of these suffered from malaria each year, with 10,000 dying from its effects. Absenteeism among students of primary and grade schools was between 40 and 50 percent daily and many large industries reported a 35-percent loss of manpower, practically all of which was attributed to the disease; each year approximately 20 million man-days of labor were lost. Eradication was started in 1957; since 1960 the average number of reported cases has fallen to 40,000 and the number of deaths each year is now less than 1,200.

The most ambitious eradication program in the world is being undertaken in India and is designed to protect more than 500 million persons. Before this campaign was started in 1953, it was estimated that 75 million people suffered from the disease each year; in 1968 the number of cases reported annually had fallen to 300,000. In the fourth five-year development plan for 1969-74 the Indian government has allocated almost $150 million for support of the program.

UNIQUE PROPERTIES OF DDT

Besides these direct benefits to health, malaria eradication has also brought impressive social and economic improvements in many areas. For example, the Terai of Uttar Pradesh in the foothills of the Himalayas has some of the most fertile terrain in India. Before malaria eradication was started, all efforts to settle and exploit it had failed. Today it is one of the most prosperous parts of the country. Malaria eradication in Ceylon also opened large tracts of previously unoccupied land to farming. In one district, over 200 square miles of such terrain was brought under irrigation and was settled by 91,000 previously landless persons.

DDT has made these achievements possible, and there is little hope that global eradication can be brought to a successful conclusion without its continued use. For many reasons, this insecticide has a number of unique advantages.

It is a biological necessity that the female of this mosquito take a blood meal before she lays her eggs, usually by seeking out man in his home during the hours of darkness. In doing so she generally rests on one of the interior wall surfaces of the house, either before or after biting. After feeding on the blood of an infected person, the mosquito must then survive for at least another 10 or 12 days before she can transmit the parasite she has thus acquired to a healthy individual. Internal wall surfaces of all human dwellings in malarious areas are therefore sprayed with an even film of insecticide, enough to kill the mosquito but too little to represent a hazard to man. In countries such as Italy and Greece, where malaria transmission occurs for no more than six months each year, one application of DDT each season is enough; in others, such as the Philippines and India, two or even three applications in each 12-month period are necessary.

DDT spraying for malaria represents little danger to ecosystems. Application is concentrated entirely indoors and directed essentially at the adult female mosquito; as males do not feed on blood, they do not enter houses to any extent and are ignored. Vegetation in the open and streams and pools and other outdoor mosquito breeding and resting places are not treated extensively with pesticides (although draining and sanitizing of breeding areas complements spraying programs). The insecticide therefore does not contaminate the general environment where it might come into contact with wildlife. As it does not in these circumstances contaminate water systems, it can have little effect on food chains and, through them, on higher organisms.

For economic reasons, amount of insecticide and frequency of application are held to a minimum compatible with efficiency. Research has shown that for the most part the insecticide thus applied remains in the body of the treated wall until the DDT breaks down chemically, particularly in homes built of mud and on wall surfaces that are re-plastered or re-covered regularly for religious or aesthetic reasons.

What are the special characteristics that make DDT so essential for malaria eradication? In the first place it has a marked ability to kill the adult anopheline mosquito. A surface treated with two grams per square meter (a one-ounce whiskey jiggerful will cover a 12- by 12-foot wall) will be lethal for periods up to six months to the intruding female mosquito. No acceptable substitute insecticide has shown itself to be persistent for more than three months.

DEADLY TO INSECTS; SAFE FOR MAN

In addition it has been particularly favorable from the viewpoint of insecticide resistance. Since the advent of the synthetic long-lasting insecticides, development of resistance has been a major challenge to entomologists. Many important insect species no longer can be controlled with DDT, and this condition has necessitated replacement of this insecticide with other suitable compounds. Notwithstanding the exposure of anopheline mosquitoes to DDT for more than two decades in almost every part of the world, however, only in one percent of the areas treated has this mosquito developed enough resistance to make malaria interruption impossible. The main reason is genetic; DDT resistance in most anopheline populations is recessive. The fact that only female mosquitoes entering houses are exposed to the insecticide is also important. This exposure limitation greatly reduces the selection that is fundamental to emergence of resistance in insect populations exposed to insecticides.

Moreover DDT has shown itself to be remarkably safe for man. Since malaria control was begun in 1945, no toxic effects have been recorded among the 200,000 or more spraymen who have been employed over long periods or among the hundreds of millions of people who have lived in houses that have been sprayed for a number of years. These observations are confirmed by extensive health monitoring in DDT factories on persons exposed to massive doses of the compound. Although some of these men had concentration in their fat 50 times as high as that found in the normal U.S. population, their general standard of health did not differ from that of the normal population. In fact the only recorded cases of DDT poisoning have been in persons who had deliberately or accidentally ingested large quantities.

Not least among the advantages of DDT is its low price. DDT is the cheapest residual insecticide yet produced in quantity, and its cost has not varied to any marked degree over the last ten years.

Large quantities of the compound are required annually to meet the needs of the global malaria program. Peak consumption was reached in 1961 when more than 64,000 tons were consumed. Even this affected only 15 percent of total world production. In 1969 the quantity used fell, and the average quantity will continue to fall as eradication is achieved.

Although the insecticide is now manufactured in a number of countries, the major source of the water-dispersible powder essential for malaria work is the United States. This country's unique ability to mass-produce a high-quality product cheaply has been vital to the development and maintenance of the global malaria program. The world is now almost completely dependent on this source of production to continue existing malaria eradication programs at their present level, to consolidate those in which eradication has almost been reached and to begin work in those countries that are still in the planning stage. If U.S.-manufactured DDT were no longer available to the developing countries a critical situation would be created. Development of alternative sources of supply elsewhere would take many years, during which time the lives and health of millions would be jeopardized.

The countries of the world are well aware of this problem and its possible consequences. The concern of India, Indonesia, Nepal, Mongolia, Ceylon, Thailand and Burma—countries in which malaria is still a major public-health problem—was clearly expressed in a resolution passed at the 22nd session of the WHO Regional Committee for Southeast Asia, held at Katmandu, Nepal, in 1969. It asked WHO to request countries producing DDT to continue to do so for the benefit of public-health programs until an equally economical insecticide could be made available in place of this insecticide.

LOOKING FOR BETTER METHODS

WHO is attempting to satisfy the urgent need for new groups of insecticides to meet the challenge of insecticide resistance and to fulfill its duty to prevent environmental pollution. During the past 12 years, in collaboration with the chemical manufacturing industry and through cooperating universities, independent institutions and field research units, it has evaluated effectiveness against insects of more than 1,400 new chemicals, with emphasis on safety to mammals and potential environmental contamination. Now available are several safe, effective and biodegradable compounds that could replace the chlorinated hydrocarbons in controlling almost every insect species of public health importance. Some of these are now in use in malaria-eradication programs in different parts of the world where resistance to DDT has occurred. These insecticides are now 12 to 20 times more expensive than DDT, however. If national health administrations were forced, through circumstances beyond their control, to turn to these new and expensive insecticides, they would be compelled to stop, or at least to reduce drastically, the level of their operating programs. An example of what might occur was recently reported from Ceylon. (I must stress that the situation there was not due entirely to lack of DDT.)

By 1963 endemic malaria had virtually disappeared from Ceylon, and the eradication program had reached a stage of consolidation and surveillance. Because of operational deficiencies, administrative problems, lack of funds and insecticides, and a series of unusual meteorological conditions, a rapid deterioration of the situation occurred from 1967 onwards. Epidemic conditions reappeared, and it has been estimated that during 1968 and 1969 considerably more than two million cases occurred with large numbers of deaths. Similar resurgences, and on a far greater scale, would inevitably occur in other countries in the process of eradication should the cost of DDT rise, or should supplies be cut off or even reduced at short notice.

WHO is also supporting an extensive program on genetic and biological controls that might reduce or even eliminate the use of chemicals for control of disease-carrying insects. With assistance from the U.S. and Indian governments a WHO Research Unit for the Genetic Control of Mosquitoes has been established in New Delhi. During the next seven years it will investigate genetic manipulation as a means of reducing mosquito populations, including the malaria carrier, *Anopheles stephensi*. In West Africa, WHO is also studying hybrid sterility, another genetic technique, as a means of controlling another malarial mosquito. WHO has been exploring predators, parasites, fungi and viruses as disease-carrier controls for ten years and will expand the program considerably in the future. However, it may be as long as ten to 15 years before any of these procedures can possibly be used operationally.

In considering continued DDT use in malaria-eradication programs, one must weigh the possible hazards against the advantages. Thus in most countries of Europe and North America, where the disease is no longer a serious problem, there is ample ecological justification for limiting its use. On the other hand, in the developing countries of the world, where malaria represents a serious social and economic problem, the continued use of the insecticide will be vital until effective and economical alternatives become available.

It would be tragic if legitimate action taken by governments to limit the use of DDT interfered with social and economic progress of developing countries. Any action taken to limit availability to these countries for purposes of ecology should be weighed carefully against the sufferings it will bring to millions and the deaths it will bring to thousands.

For Discussion and Review

1. What health benefits does Wright claim for DDT? How do these benefits compare with the detrimental health effects that Rachel Carson cites in regard to pesticides in general?
2. What method of spraying does Wright recommend? What are the advantages? Do you think Carson would approve of his recommendation? Why or why not?
3. Assume you have the authority to control the use and manufacture of DDT. Would you incorporate some of the information in Wright's article into the guidelines you set up? Explain.

Hello Energy. Good-bye Big Sky

BY JOHN NEARY

The tough old Southwest, a place of deceptive beauty canopied by a Cinerama sky, has always been a battleground. Long before men started in on the area, volcanoes blasted it, glaciers honed it and seas tided across it, sculpting the mesas where dinosaurs left their big-toed tracks. Civilization sets uneasily on the land even now, tentative and merely temporary, barely able to hold its own in this place. Here are bears, rattlesnakes, tarantulas as big as hand grenades, cactuses tough enough to spike through a $20 boot. Here are pale scorpions fond of cuddling into sleeping bags away from the night chill and gangs of crazy coyotes that scream into your dreams like sad lost banshees in the mountain dawn. This old land has always scaled men down fast—those foolish enough to fight it—and it abounds in mocking reminders of the arrogant intruders who wandered in looking to conquer it: some broken armor, some potsherds, some battered icons, some flaked flint points. Coronado was here hunting for the Seven Cities of Cibola; others since have come looking, too, with more luck, finding gold, silver, copper, lead, uranium and oil. But the land prevailed.

In recent years a new generation of seekers, outfitted with equipment that would dwarf Coronado's armada, has arrived to harvest no such glittering booty. They are after coal to fuel the enormous electrical generating plants they are constructing nearby. And what burning that coal does to the air will change the look of the land forever.

My friend Rex Arrowsmith, geologist and Indian trader, knows intimately the old conflicts and the present struggles. In his shop in Santa

---

John Neary, a former newspaperman with the *Washington Star,* has also been an Associate Editor for *Life* magazine. He has written numerous articles and short stories and is the author of a recent book, *Julian Bond: Black Rebel.*

John Neary, "Hello, Energy—Good-bye, Big Sky," *Life*, April 16, 1971, pp. 61–71. Reprinted by permission.

Fe, crowded with pieces of Spanish harness and worn carbines, polished silver and old smooth turquoise, Arrowsmith showed me a thick study by the Arizona Bureau of Mines reporting the presence of an estimated 20 billion short tons of coal at Black Mesa, near where the four corners of New Mexico, Arizona, Colorado and Utah meet.

Hello, energy. Goodbye, big sky.

One crisp morning last fall in Los Alamos, N. Mex.—which is some 7,000 feet above sea level, about 30 miles north of Santa Fe—I walked out into the backyard of my in-laws' house where I have visited off and on for the past 12 years. I walked down through the big pines, scuffing through the thin mantle of needles that carpeted the soft tuff rock, toward the rim of the little canyon at the foot of the lot. Accommodating the profusion of nature—the ornate detail of tree bark, and the delicate hue of a lichened rock, the astounding blue sky through the grainy etched tapestry of the trees—takes as much getting used to as does breathing the thin sharp air. I stopped at the rim and looked out across the Rio Grande valley to the Sangre de Cristos mountains, 40 to 50 miles to the southwest. And it was not the way it used to be.

When I first came out here from the East a dozen years ago it was like having the bandages taken off after an eye operation. As I stepped out on the platform between cars on the Super Chief rolling into Lamy, the bright red soil and the brilliant green sage slammed my vision with a clarity and force I'd never seen before. Folks back home who'd never been here, I realized sadly, grew up and died without ever having really *seen*. Then, you could stand where I was standing now and make out every detail on those massive mountains, just as, from the slope above Los Alamos after sundown, you could see the twinkling lights of Albuquerque about 55 miles away.

But this morning the mountains were just a silhouette in ink wash, a vague gray somberness, like the mountains in Pennsylvania or West Virginia. Above the tips of the pines across the canyon was just a hint of a heavy grayness, that same darkening of tone you can see looking from the Atlantic toward Long Island and New York City—a shadowy, smudgy cobweb of smog lying on the horizon.

Standing here on the mesa where Los Alamos is, on the edge of Pajarito Plateau, you now realize that you know something absolutely awful: that very same dark miasma, that overhanging penumbra of soot and dirt and ash and photochemical smog, stretches all the way now. All the way across the North American continent. All the way from the lip of the Atlantic across the Alleghenies and the Piedmont, across the prairie, over the Rockies and beyond, to the Pacific ashtrays of Los Angeles and San Francisco. Now you know that the last stretch of wide-open space we had left, the American Southwestern skyscape, is gone, too.

I met Jack Loeffler, a writer who lives on a low bluff outside Santa Fe; his living room window gives onto hundreds of square miles of forbiddingly lovely terrain, fenced in only by the mountains. "I've been looking out that window for four years," Loeffler said, "and that view diminishes annually."

This rather subjective determination by Loeffler and me, that we couldn't see as far as we used to, has been reached by a more expert observer, Joe Devaney of Los Alamos. Devaney, a physicist who likes to fly his own plane, noticed the visibility of the area was deteriorating when, one day in 1966 on his way back from a hop to the Grand Canyon, he glanced down at where his instruments said the city of Farmington, N. Mex., should have been. No Farmington. Devaney's watch was right and so was his math; the problem simply was that thick blanket of heavy smoke covering the earth beneath his wings, pouring out of the stacks of the new electric plant at Fruitland, not far from Farmington.

Curious at how far the smoke went, Devaney proceeded to follow it. "I'd been flying around like a guy born into money," he marvels now. "We had clean air—the cleanest air possible. Before '66 the curvature of the earth was the limiting thing. We could see 120 miles and more at 10,000 feet. Last summer visibility at Los Alamos dropped to as low as seven miles."

The Fruitland plant, Devaney discovered, was filling up the vast natural basin between the Rockies and the Jemez Mountains like a backed-up bathtub drain, and the area's winds were sloshing the smoke around all the way from Taos to Albuquerque. Worse, Devaney discovered, much of the smoke is made up of tiny, submicron-sized particles of fly ash which, unlike the heavier chunks that settle quickly to the ground, stay in the air for days, weeks, months, perhaps even longer.

Joe Devaney decided to do something about this situation. First he shot pictures of the effects of the smoke upon the vistas he saw through the windscreen of his plane, and he showed the pictures to any audience he could persuade to sit still. Then he began speaking to "anyone who would give me a hearing"—which meant two trips to Washington to buttonhole New Mexico's congressional delegation, 15 trips down to the state legislature and uncounted evenings before local service clubs. Devaney totes up his success to date: "Zero, or nearly so."

Despite his efforts—and he was joined by such groups as the John Muir Institute, the Sierra Club, the League of Women Voters, the Central Clearing House and the Black Mesa Defense of Santa Fe—Devaney and his fellow antismoggers see Southwestern air pollution increasing. To understand exactly how this can be so, it is necessary to head north from Los Alamos, to take a look at the Fruitland plant.

The odometer read 7440 when I first spotted the plume of smoke from the plant, just after I had passed the Huerfano trading post near the turnoff to Chaco Canyon. But it was not until another 50 miles had passed that the plant itself came into view. You get to it by driving down the narrow two-lane blacktop through Fruitland, under the drooping willows and cottonwoods, past the yellow-blooming chamis and the roadside stands aglow with heaping baskets of Golden Delicious apples. Then across the skinny little San Juan River and head up the hill onto Indian land. Here, on the Navajo reservation, lies the black magnet that has drawn the power company: coal.

Thirty miles off to the west sits Shiprock, high as the Empire State Building, an ancient landmark for travelers across these badlands. Today, however, it is as dimly visible as the towers of Manhattan's Battery in the harbor smog, because Shiprock is awash in the drifting smoke from the coal-burning power plant's stacks. Nearly 300 tons of coal ash a day come floating up out of those stacks, the unfortunate by-product of the manufacture of 2,085 megawatts of electricity for consumers in Albuquerque, Phoenix, El Paso, Tucson and Los Angeles (where, ironically, such a plant could not now be built).

For many of the Navajo Indians, who own the land upon which it sits, and their paleface neighbors, the plant is a welcome newcomer to the area in spite of all the smoke. The reason is simple: money. Informed of the fact that still another plant was to be built nearby, the Farmington *Daily Times* rejoiced on its editorial page: "Whee! We'd like to add our reaction to the news that there's going to be another mammoth power plant in this area. An $11-million-a-year payroll for 450 workers, which is the estimate during construction, will be a welcome stimulant to our economy, as will the more than half-million dollar payroll after the plant goes into operation. That's what we call progress—and we're all for it. Whee, again!"

Still more plants are projected for the vast region surrounding the "Four Corners" area. A single mine, atop Black Mesa, will supply coal for two plants, one at Page, Ariz., on the shore of Lake Powell, and another named Mohave on the California-Nevada border. Others are being considered for the Kaiparowits Plateau across Lake Powell and for Huntington, Utah. To assuage conservationists' fears that the Four Corners region will become another Hoboken, the power companies say they are doing everything possible to cleanse their stack emissions of dangerous matter—both visible and invisible.

For example, by the end of this year, stacks at the Farmington plant will be outfitted with new, more effective precipitators that will reduce the present fly-ash output of almost 300 tons by nearly 90%. But even with the best possible pollution controls, former Los Alamos engineer Mike Williams estimates, all six projected power plants will, when operating, be pumping daily some 2,160 tons of sulphur dioxide and 850 to 1,300 tons of nitrogen oxide (both of which are key ingredients of smog). And despite such improvements as those at Farmington, says Williams, there will *still* be as much as 240 tons of coal ash—only 50 tons less than New York and Los Angeles combined—emitted into into the air each day. Whee!

Some Indians, unaware of both the economic and the ecologic impact of all this, are mystified by the sudden change in a landscape that had been as changeless as their legends. Buck Austin, a 64-year-old Navajo who has always lived on the windy crest of Black Mesa, paused in the building of a new hogan to tell me through a translator that Navajo Mountain—an important tribal shrine that had been visible 50 miles to the north as long as he could remember—had simply vanished in the filthy air.

Other Indians are angry over the mine and the power plant. "It's just genocide," said one young Yakima Indian, who moved to the Southwest from the West Coast to join the fight against the power plants. "L.A. and Phoenix have more population, so if the Hopi and the Navajo have got to go so that somebody in L.A. can watch color television, that's the way it is—that's the way it's always been."

But there are other Indians, too, who suspect there might be some good in the coal mines and the power plants. Newly elected Navajo Tribal Council Chairman Peter MacDonald is one; he wants to review the leases between the power companies and the tribe to see "if there is a way to have the Navajo tribe gain as much from these operations as the coal and power companies." They, MacDonald estimates, will realize close to a billion dollars over 25 years, while the Navajos will get only $15 or $20 million. "That," says MacDonald, "is something the Navajo needs to reconsider."

Still, to some Indians, there are even more important things than millions or billions of dollars or the white man's infatuation with electricity. Wiry, compact Fred Kabotie, 74, mused upon this as he stood in the sun-washed showroom of the Hopi Cultural Center that he persuaded his tribe to build. Kabotie, who travels regularly to New York to advise the Louis Comfort Tiffany Foundation on the training of young artists, spoke of the danger that something called "the slurry line" will drain the water table on Black Mesa and thus parch the tribal grazing land. The slurry, an 18-inch buried pipe, will suck 120,000 gallons of water every hour from deep beneath the grazing land atop the mesa, mix it with the 660 tons of finely powdered coal and sluice it across the desert to the Mohave plant. Kabotie also wondered whether Indians will really get jobs in the mine and at the power plant.

The power companies vehemently contend they have taken into consideration all these concerns in placing, designing and operating their mines and plants. Wells to feed the slurry will go far deeper than the water level tapped by Indian herders, they say, and they have made assurances that once the coal has been mined, careful reseeding and landscaping of the strip mine area will be carried out—if the profits allow it.

But always the primary pressure is the power companies' well-justified apprehension that unless they move fast, good old Reddy Kilowatt just might not be there with the juice when some new customer throws the switch. It is a perfectly reasonable position. Says L. M. Alexander, associate general manager of the Salt River Project, a public authority charged with providing water and electricity to meet Arizona's burgeoning demands: "Our responsibilities as utilities are to make certain there is enough electricity to operate every air-conditioner, heater and other type of electrical appliance our customers may want to use. They dictate—it is up to us to respond."

It is, of course, that fearsome prospect of a power shortage and not some malevolent intent which has brought the utilities into such harsh conflict with those Southwesterners who put their land and its beauty above convenience and progress.

The electric power people and the mining companies operate under overlapping and often confusing sets of pollution controls set by federal agencies, counties and states—each jurisdiction zealously cautious lest it drive away a potential bonanza by too-stringent regulation. New Mexico's Clinton P. Anderson plans to begin holding Senate Interior Committee hearings next month to determine, as an aide puts it, "what's wrong and what will go wrong. It's mind-boggling, trying to figure out just who has done what. It's a mess." Power companies and their opponents now appear to be heading for a courtroom resolution of their differences, irreconcilable though they may seem.

Defining the venue of the case will be difficult: local, state or federal? Which locality, which states, and if federal, then are not all of us potential jurors? Can any of us, we operators of electric toothbrushes, Water Piks, slot car sets, electric carving knives, hair dryers, lathes, television sets, divest ourselves of our complicity? Of our bone-deep stake in the perpetuation of the beauty of our own Southwest? Can any of us who can see really declare, as plantiff and defendant pick over the veniremen, that we know nothing of the case—have smelled nothing? Do we not all have a conflict of interest?

Heading out of Albuquerque one evening, I found myself driving into one of those three-ring, 3-D, cycloramic scenic extravaganzas the Southwest stages every few sunsets. It was not one of those paltry pink fizzes we exult over back on Long Island, but the kind of sunset performance you could expect from an earth that had taken a few million spins to whomp it up. It had a little bit of everything. The lights of the city lay behind me and I saw in the rear-view mirror a winking, blinking earthbound constellation of electrically powered red, gold and green—a man-made nightscape all our own. Ahead, the sunset lay on the northwestern skyline like molten iron. Far off, flat gray clouds flecked the deep orange of the sky, while nearer, a fat little smoke-puff of a rain cloud loosed a shower toward the burnt and empty land, down onto the silhouettes of tumbleweed. Venus shone brightly through the pale gray-blue of the sky above me, and a crescent moon glared through a misty cloud head directly beneath it. The layered mountains to my right were almost completely curtained off by the storm.

It was a sky so wide my eye could not scan it, so wildly beautiful, so variegated in color and emotion from ferocious storm to gentle calm, that I could not comprehend the idea that anyone could think of selling it.

For Discussion and Review

1. How have the coal companies responded to the main concerns of the Indians? Discuss whether or not you find the coal companies' response acceptable.
2. Why do you think it will be difficult to define the venue of the case between the power companies and their opponents? What aspects of the case fall within the jurisdiction of several governmental units?
3. What value conflicts does Neary's article point up? What other recent controversies have contained the same kinds of conflicts?

Preserving Our Environment

BY JAMES MICHENER

Observers believe that the quality of life in the United States will be determined by what steps we take to safeguard the environment in which we live. They point with apprehension to the rapid rate at which we are polluting our air, contaminating our water supply, killing off our wild life and raising the noise level of our cities. They call these processes "the uglification of America," with special emphasis on the unplanned manner in which our cities reach out to create ever new urban sprawl.

I agree with these critics. Years ago I decided that even though I was free to live anywhere in the world, I would stick with rural Bucks County, for I had seen nothing in my travels which surpassed it in its simple combination of natural beauty, orderliness and nearness to the big cities that I have enjoyed so much. I have never regretted that choice, for life in this part of the Philadelphia area is almost as good as it could be.

Other people might prefer other places: Princeton, New Jersey, and Santa Barbara, California, have been mentioned as nearly ideal spots in which to live, combining as they do a natural beauty with cultural richness. But the arrival of an oil slick has destroyed much of the attractiveness of the latter site. Certain villages in New England, wholly in the countryside yet close to Boston, have a similar quality, and several areas on the Main Line west of Philadelphia are better managed than the area in which I live, but on balance I picked a good spot.

James Michener, who won the Pulitzer Prize in 1947 for his *Tales of the South Pacific*, has written fifteen books and edited and coauthored several others. In recent years he is best known for *Hawaii* and *The Source*, which like his other works reveal his interest in nature.

What has happened? Every year of my life the land between where I live and Philadelphia has become more jumbled, more abused and uglier. And along the main highways which take me into New York the deterioration has been appalling, with forty miles of unplanned monstrosities degrading the countryside and cheapening the lives of people who live there or who pass through. Dirt, noise, ugliness, pollution and lack of care characterize this drift away from natural beauty and into a new kind of urban blight.

Let me be specific as to what I mean by this criticism and what I do not mean. I will specify the latter first.

When I was in my late teens, one of the joys of my life was traveling from Doylestown westward through Norristown to Valley Forge and down to Villanova and Swarthmore, where I was attending college. It was a journey through the best part of America, with birds and flowers and now and then a sight of deer in the distant fields. I remember with special delight how exciting it was to cross the beautiful Schuylkill River at Norristown and enter that lovely maze of roads leading to rural King of Prussia, Valley Forge and the rolling hills to the south. I never traveled this road in either direction without feeling privileged.

The other day I had occasion to make this trip again and found the area to be an undifferentiated suburb, one house or establishment after another, plus a whole new city at King of Prussia. I could have had no more dramatic introduction to the problem of conserving our natural resources than this, for the city had reached out and gobbled up one of the loveliest areas I had known.

Well, I did not object. And I do not sympathize with mere protesters who cry, "Isn't it a shame that King of Prussia has become a city?" or "Isn't it deplorable that a Levittown had to spring up in lower Bucks County?" If the area population is going to grow from 1,900,000 in 1900 to 7,500,000 in 2000, people are going to have to live somewhere and I think the creation of whole new communities is one of the sensible answers. Within the next thirty years, if our area population increases by 2,000,000, we will have to provide 500,000 new homes and they will have to go somewhere.

Changes in our patterns of local government must come if these newcomers are to find land for their houses. Our courts have begun to throw out many of the zoning ordinances used by suburban communities to keep city dwellers and other strangers out. A tight circle of exclusiveness circumscribing the city cannot be tolerated, and ordinances calling for two-acre plots or even one-acre will be declared illegal if they are too near the city and held to be operating against the general welfare. We will not then be able to ensure suburban beauty merely by maintaining large expanses of lawn; we will also have to look to the beauty of what we build on the land thus set free.

The physical look of the entire area, from the most rural edge of the New Jersey counties to the most exclusive residential areas of the Main Line, will be sharply modified. In the last five years, within a mile from my remote rural home, a dozen new houses have been built, and before long it will be a hundred. It ought to be, for homes are needed.

Therefore I do not see how one can logically object to the mushrooming of new communities or the services that tend them, which means that we shall soon be living in one unbroken urban area reaching from Washington to Boston. We cannot halt this, granted our rapid growth of population, but we can take steps to see that the growth is logical and that it preserves as much natural beauty as possible.

What I do object to is this: For the past several years my neighbors have mentioned from time to time the serious pollution of an historic stream that runs not far from my home. I listened vaguely but did nothing about it. Then Joe Livingston, the financial columnist, told me, "You've got to go down and see what's happened." So I went.

This marvelous stream in which I used to fish and where as a boy I had gone swimming, this ribbon of cool water which had been a delight to generations of farmers, was now a fetid body of yellowish water with not a living thing in it. Frogs, fish, waterlilies, bullrushes and ducks' nests had all vanished, and along the edges of the swimming hole stood shameful signs, posted by the health department: WARNING—DO NOT USE THIS WATER FOR SWIMMING— UNSAFE FOR BATHING.

When I inspected the stream, I found that an acid deposit perhaps an eighth of an inch thick had been cast upon the whole stream bed; this had killed every living thing, even the weeds, along the entire length of the stream to the point where it emptied into the Delaware.

What had happened? A responsible manufacturing company, which had brought much-needed jobs into our community and which we had welcomed, found it expedient to dump its chemical waste into the stream. The local court had enjoined the company from doing this, but enforcement of the order had been impossible, so that now one of our most charming natural resources had been destroyed. (Experts assure us that if the deposit of new waste is halted, three or four years of flushing out with pure water will restore the stream. A decade of therapeutic attention might even restore Lake Erie, for nature's powers of recovery are phenomenal, as reforestation has proved.)

The loss of my stream had occurred under my nose, as it were, and with me making no protest. When I finally saw what had happened, I was ashamed of my inattention. What in those years had I been doing that was more important than saving a stream? If we continue to abuse and destroy our resources, many of us will be asking that question thirty years from now, but by then it will be too late, and some of the precious things we have lost will not be recoverable.

Shortly after publication of the preceding paragraphs, dramatic proof was given of the unexpected way a ravaged environment can strike back at the persons who have abused it. When we made public outcry against the contamination of our stream, the manufacturing company built a series of deep catchment basins into which they pumped their poisonous waste. This was not a solution to the problem, merely a postponement; the life-killing contaminants continued to seep through the bottom of the basins and into the stream in the same old way. But since the amount of flow was somewhat diminished, the visible effect was less frightening than it had been, and some of us concluded that this temporizing measure had settled the problem. The stream wouldn't be totally poisoned, only half so.

Then our area was faced with one of those ten-year cyclic accidents of a heavy snow followed immediately by a warm rain. Our valley was flooded, roads were washed out, farmers were marooned, and an unusually high crest of water threatened to overflow the manufacturing plant, flush out the catchment basins and throw 50,000 gallons of lead sulfate into our trivial little stream—and from it into the heart of the Delaware River, from which some five million people take their drinking water.

Faced by a disaster of such proportions, crews of my neighbors were summoned to pile sandbags about the catchment basins to keep the poison from overflowing. Only their strenuous efforts protected the drinking supply of a metropolitan area, and at last our whole community awakened to the monster we had allowed to grow up in our back yard. It had killed a stream. Now it could kill us.

I am not a primitivist. I do not automatically think that old ways are best, and nothing seems more inane to me than the argument that life was somehow better in colonial times because farm wives made their own soap and candles. As a boy I studied by lamplight and had to wash the lamp chimneys, and believe me, electricity is better. I am often asked if the natives in the South Pacific were not happier before the advent of canned goods and penicillin, and I counter with the question, "Were the people happier when the life expectancy of a woman was thirty-five and a man thirty-nine?"

I am for change, and when it also represents progress I am happy. Let me explain further what I mean. One of the reasons I live where I do is that often in the morning or in the late afternoon I can see herds of deer browsing in the fields not far from where I work. I never cease to thrill at the sight of these splendid animals who share the woods with me. What have they been worth to me: untold values in relaxation and the appreciation of nature.

I am quite prepared for the fact that within a few years the pressure of population in my area will force the deer to move on. Ten years from now they will not be visible at dusk, and that will be a loss, but it will be offset by the good that the new residents in the area will enjoy from living in new homes and spacious surroundings.

Therefore I can accept the disappearance of the deer from my front lawn, but if they were to disappear altogether, as many species might if natural living areas are not preserved, I should experience a loss so great that I am not sure I would want to go on living in a world that had sacrificed so much. A good society does not require that the deer live on my lawn, but it does require that they live somewhere.

This planet, devoid of its natural inhabitants—animals and birds and fish and trees and flowers—would be a desolation. It is quite possible that men require dogs and deer to keep them human. It is possible that we need cleaner air and quieter cities to keep us sane. There is a balance between beauty and business that must not be ignored.

The quality of a good life depends in large measure on how a man reacts to his natural environment, and we cannot destroy one without diminishing the other.

Fortunately, in this area we are facing up to the problem in time. Not far from my home, four parks now operate and a fifth is about to come into being. The ravages we have permitted can be reversed. Space will be provided so that animals and birds can survive with us, and the good architecture at King of Prussia proves that the new cities which will replace the old farms can be appealing to the eye. Whether we can halt air pollution and the rapid rise in the noise level remains to be seen, but at least we have been alerted to the problem. In thirty years my hill will be completely altered. It need not be destroyed.

For Discussion and Review

1. How might Michener react to the proposed construction of a highway through a park to relieve massive traffic congestion on the outskirts of a city?
2. Why does Michener agree with recent court actions that have overruled zoning ordinances?
3. What does Michener means when he says, "I am for a change, and when it represents progress, I am happy"? Do you agree with Michener's position on preserving the environment? Why or why not?

SOLUTION

We need a religious system with science at its very core, in which the traditional opposition between science and religion, reflected in grisly truth by our technologically desecrated countryside, can again be resolved, but in terms of the future instead of the past.
—Margaret Mead

It seems to me that our ideals, laws and customs should be based on the proposition that each generation, in turn, becomes the custodian rather than the absolute owner of our resources—and each generation has the obligation to pass this inheritance on to the future.
—Charles Lindbergh

Animals have no souls; therefore, according to the most authoritative Christian theologians, they may be treated as though they were things. The truth . . . is that even things ought not to be treated as **mere** things. They should be treated as though they were parts of a vast living organism. . . . The Golden Rule applies to our dealings with nature no less than our dealings with our fellow-men. If we hope to be well treated by nature, we must stop talking about "mere things" and start treating our planet with intelligence and consideration.
—Aldous Huxley

Think Little

BY WENDELL BERRY

First there was Civil Rights, and then there was The War, and now it is The Environment. The first two of this sequence of causes have already risen to the top of the nation's consciousness and declined somewhat in a remarkably short time. I mention this in order to begin with what I believe to be justifiable skepticism. For it seems to me that the Civil Rights Movement and the Peace Movement, as popular causes in the electronic age, have partaken far too much of the nature of fads. Not for all, certainly, but for too many they have been the fashionable politics of the moment. As causes they have been under-taken too much in ignorance; they have been too much simplified; they have been powered too much by impatience and guilt of conscience and short-term enthusiasm, and too little by an authentic social vision and long-term conviction and deliberation. For most people those causes have remained almost entirely abstract; there has been too little personal involvement, and too much involvement in organizations which were insisting that *other* organizations should do what was right.

There is considerable danger that the Environment Movement will have the same nature: that it will be a public cause, served by organi-zations that will self-righteously criticize and condemn other organi-zations, inflated for a while by a lot of public talk in the media, only to be replaced in its turn by another fashionable crisis. I hope that will not happen, and I believe that there are ways to keep it from happen-

Wendell Berry, a poet and farmer with a strong affection for his native Kentucky, has been very active in anti-strip-mining movements in his state. He is currently Professor of Creative Writing at the University of Kentucky, and his works include *The Long-Legged House, The Hidden Wound,* and *The Unforeseen Wilderness.*

Wendell Berry, "Think Little," *Blue Tail Fly,* November 7, 1970. Reprinted by permission of the author.

ing, but I know that if this effort is carried on solely as a public cause, if millions of people cannot or will not undertake it as a *private* cause as well, then it is *sure* to happen. In five years the energy of our present concern will have petered out in a series of public gestures—and no doubt in a series of empty laws—and a great, and perhaps the last, human opportunity will have been lost.

It need not be that way. A better possibility is that the movement to preserve the environment will be seen to be, as I think it has to be, not a digression from the civil rights and peace movements, but the logical culmination of those movements. For I believe that the separation of these three problems is artificial. They have the same cause, and that is the mentality of greed and exploitation. The mentality that exploits and destroys the natural environment is the same that abuses racial and economic minorities, that imposes on young men the tyranny of the military draft, that makes war against peasants and women and children with the indifference of technology. The mentality that destroys a watershed and then panics at the threat of flood is the same mentality that gives institutionalized insult to black people and then panics at the prospect of race riots. It is the same mentality that can mount deliberate warfare against a civilian population and then express moral shock at the logical consequences of such warfare at My Lai. We would be fools to believe that we could solve any one of these problems without solving the others.

To me, one of the most important aspects of the environmental movement is that it brings us not just to another public crisis, but to a crisis of the protest movement itself. For the environmental crisis should make it dramatically clear, as perhaps it has not always been before, that there is no public crisis that is not also private. To most advocates of civil rights racism has seemed mostly the fault of someone else. For most advocates of peace the war has been a remote reality, and the burden of the blame has seemed to rest mostly on the government. I am certain that these crises have been more private, and that we have each suffered more from them and been more responsible for them, than has been readily apparent, but the connections have been difficult to see. Racism and militarism have been institutionalized among us for too long for our personal involvement in those evils to be easily apparent to us. Think, for example, of all the Northerners who assumed—until black people attempted to move into *their* neighborhoods—that racism was a Southern phenomenon. And think how quickly—one might almost say how naturally—among some of its members the peace movement has spawned policies of deliberate provocation and violence.

But the environmental crisis rises closer to home. Every time we draw a breath, every time we drink a glass of water, every time we eat a bite of food we are suffering from it. And more important, every time we indulge in, or depend on, the wastefulness of our economy—and our economy's first principle is waste—we are *causing* the crisis. Nearly every one of us, nearly every day of his life, is contributing *directly* to the ruin of this planet. A protest meeting on the issue of environmental abuse is not a convocation of accusers, it is a convocation of the guilty. That realization ought to clear the smog of self-righteousness that has almost conventionally hovered over these occasions, and let us see the work that is to be done.

In this crisis it is certain that every one of us has a public responsibility. We must not cease to bother the government and the other institutions, to see that they never become comfortable with easy promises. For myself, I want to say that I hope never again to go to Frankfort [Kentucky] to present a petition to the governor on an issue so vital as that of strip mining, only to be dealt with by some ignorant functionary—as several of us were not so long ago, the governor himself being "too busy" to receive us. Next time I will go prepared to wait as long as necessary to see that the petitioners' complaints and their arguments are heard *fully*—and by the governor. And then I will hope to find ways to keep those complaints and arguments from being forgotten until something is done to relieve them. The time is past when it was enough merely to elect our officials. We will have to elect them and then go and *watch* them and keep our hands on them, the way the coal companies do. We have made a tradition in Kentucky of putting self-servers, and worse, in charge of our vital interests. I am sick of it. And I think that one way to change it is to make Frankfort a less comfortable place. I believe in American political principles, and I will not sit idly by and see those principles destroyed by sorry practice. I am ashamed and deeply distressed that American government should have become the chief cause of disillusionment with American principles.

And so when the government in Frankfort again proves too stupid or too blind or too corrupt to see the plain truth and to act with simple decency, I intend to be there, and I trust that I won't be alone. I hope, moreover, to be there, not with a sign or a slogan or a button, but with the facts and the arguments. A crowd whose discontent has risen no higher than the level of slogans is *only* a crowd. But a crowd that understands the reasons for its discontent and knows the remedies is a vital community, and it will have to be reckoned with. I would rather go before the government with two men who have a competent understanding of an issue, and who therefore deserve a hearing, than to go with two thousand who are vaguely dissatisfied.

But even the most articulate public protest is not enough. We don't live in the government or in institutions or in our public utterances and acts, and the environmental crisis has its roots in our *lives*. By the same token, environmental health will also be rooted in our lives. That is, I take it, simply a fact, and in the light of it we can see how superficial and foolish we would be to think that we could correct what is wrong merely by tinkering with the institutional machinery. The changes that are required are fundamental changes in the way we are living.

What we are up against in this country, in any attempt to involve private responsibility, is that we have nearly destroyed private life. Our people have given up their independence in return mostly for the cheap seductions and the shoddy merchandise of so-called affluence. We have delegated all our vital functions and responsibilities to salesmen and agents and bureaus and experts of all sorts. We cannot feed or clothe ourselves, or entertain ourselves, or communicate with each other, or be charitable or neighborly or loving, or even respect ourselves, without recourse to a merchant or a corporation or a public service organization or an agency of the government or a style-setter or an expert. Most of us cannot think of dissenting from the opinions or the actions of one organization without first forming a new organization. Individualism is going around these days in uniform, handing out the party line on individualism. Dissenters want to publish their personal opinions over a thousand signatures.

The Confucian *Great Digest* says that the "chief way for the production of wealth" (and he is talking about real goods, not money) is "that the producers be many and that the mere consumers be few. . . ." But even in the much publicized rebellion of the young against the materialism of the affluent society, the consumer mentality is too often still intact: the standards of behavior are still those of kind and quantity, the security sought is still the security of numbers, and the chief motive is still the consumer's anxiety that one is missing out on what is "in." In this state of total consumerism—which is to say a state of helpless dependence on things and services and ideas and motives that we have forgotten how to provide ourselves—all meaningful contact between ourselves and the earth is broken. We do not understand the earth either in terms of what it offers us or what it requires of us, and I think it is the rule that people inevitably destroy what they do not understand. Most of us are not directly responsible for strip mining and extractive agriculture and other forms of environmental abuse. But we are guilty nevertheless, for we connive in them by our ignorance. We are ignorantly dependent on them. We do not know enough about them; we do not have a particular enough sense of their damage. Most of us, for example, not only do not know how to produce the best food in the best way—we don't know how to produce any kind in any way. And for this condition we have elaborate rationalizations, instructing us that dependence for everything on somebody else is efficient and economical and a scientific miracle. I say, instead, that it is madness, mass produced. A man who understands the weather only in terms of golf is participating in a chronic public insanity that either he or his descendents will be bound to realize as suffering. I believe that the death of the world is breeding in such minds much more certainly and much faster than in any political capital or atomic arsenal.

For an index of our loss of contact with the earth we need only to look at the condition of the American farmer—who must in our society, as in every society, enact man's dependence on the land, and his responsibility to it. In an age of unparalleled affluence and leisure, the American farmer is harder pressed and harder worked than ever before; his margin of profit is small, his hours long; his outlays for land and equipment and the expenses of maintenance and operation are growing rapidly greater; he cannot compete with industry for labor; he is being forced more and more to depend on the use of destructive chemicals and on the wasteful methods of haste and anxiety. As a class, farmers are one of the despised minorities. So far as I can see farming is considered marginal or incidental to the economy of the country, and farmers, when they are thought of at all, are thought of as hicks and yokels, whose lives do not fit into the modern scene. The average American farmer is now an old man, whose sons have moved away to the cities. His knowledge, and his intimate connection with the land are about to be lost. The small independent farmer is going the way of the small independent craftsmen and storekeepers. He is being forced off the land into the cities, his place taken by absentee owners, corporations, and machines. Some would justify all this in the name of efficiency. As I see it, it is an enormous social and economic and cultural blunder. For the small farmers who lived on their farms *cared* about their land. And given their established connection to their land —which was often hereditary and traditional as well as economic— they could have been encouraged to care for it more competently than they have so far. The corporations and machines that replace them will never be bound to the land by the sense of birthright and continuity, or by the love which enforces care. They will be bound by the rule of efficiency which takes thought only of the volume of the year's produce, and takes no thought of the slow increment of the life of the land, not measurable in pounds or dollars, which will assure the livelihood and the health of the coming generations.

If we are to hope to correct our abuses of each other and of other races and of our land, and if our effort to correct these abuses is to be more than a political fad that will in the long run be only another form of abuse, then we are going to have to go far beyond public protest and political action. We are going to have to rebuild the substance and the integrity of private life in this country. We are going to have to gather up the fragments of knowledge and responsibility that we have parceled out to the bureaus and the corporations and the specialists, and we are going to have to put those fragments back together again in our own minds and in our families and households and neighborhoods. We need better government, no doubt about it. But we also need better minds, better friendships, better marriages, better communities. We need persons and households that do not need to wait upon organizations but who can make necessary changes in themselves, on their own.

For most of the history of this country our motto, implied or spoken, has been Think Big. I have come to believe that a better motto, and an essential one now, is Think Little. That implies the necessary change of thinking and feeling, and suggests the necessary work. Thinking Big has led us to the two biggest and cheapest political dodges of our time: plan-making and law-making. The lotus-eaters of this era are in Washington D.C., Thinking Big. Somebody comes up with a problem, and somebody in the government comes up with a plan or a law. The result, mostly, has been the persistence of the problem, and the enlargement and enrichment of the government.

But the discipline of thought is not generalization; it is detail, and it is personal behavior. While the government is "studying" and funding and organizing its Big Thought, nothing is being done. But the citizen who is willing to think little, and, accepting the discipline of that, to go ahead on his own, is already solving the problem. A man who is trying to live as a neighbor to his neighbors will have a lively and practical understanding of the work of peace and brotherhood, and let there be no mistake about it—he is *doing* that work. A couple who makes a good marriage, and raise healthy, morally competent children are serving the world's future more directly and surely than any political leader, though they never utter a public word. A good farmer who is dealing with the problem of soil erosion on an acre of ground has a sounder grasp of that problem, and *cares* more about it, and is probably doing more to solve it than any bureaucrat who is talking about it in general. A man who is willing to undertake the discipline and the difficulty of mending his own ways is worth more to the conservation movement than a hundred who are insisting merely that the government and the industries mend *their* ways.

If you are concerned about the proliferation of trash, then by all means start an organization in your community to do something about it. But before—*and while*—you organize, pick up some cans and bottles yourself. That way, at least, you will assure yourself and others that you mean what you say. If you are concerned about air pollution, help push for government controls, but drive your car less, use less fuel in your home. If you are worried about the damming of wilderness rivers, join the Sierra Club, write to the government, but turn off the lights you're not using, don't install an air conditioner, don't be a sucker for electrical gadgets, don't waste water. In other words, if you are fearful of the destruction of the environment, then learn to quit being an environmental parasite. We all are, in one way or another, and the remedies are not always obvious, though they certainly will always be difficult. They require a new kind of life—harder, more laborious, poorer in luxuries and gadgets, but also, I am certain, richer in meaning and more abundant in real pleasure. To have a healthy environment we will all have to give up things we like; we may even have to give up things we have come to think of as necessities. But to be fearful of the disease and yet unwilling to pay for the cure is not just to be hypocritical; it is to be doomed. If you talk a good line without being changed by what you say, then you are not just hypocritical and doomed; you have become an agent of the disease. Consider, for an example, the President, who advertises his grave concern about the destruction of the environment, and who turns up the air conditioner to make it cool enough to build a fire.

Odd as I am sure it will appear to some, I can think of no better form of personal involvement in the cure of the environment than that of gardening. A person who is growing a garden, if he is growing it organically, is improving a piece of the world. He is producing something to eat, which makes him somewhat independent of the grocery business, but he is also enlarging, for himself, the meaning of food and the pleasure of eating. The food he grows will be fresher, more nutritious, less contaminated by poisons and preservatives and dye, than what he can buy at a store. He is reducing the trash problem; a garden is not a disposable container, and it will digest and re-use its own wastes. If he enjoys working in his garden, then he is less dependent on an automobile or a merchant for his pleasure. He is involving himself directly in the work of feeding people.

If you think I'm wandering off the subject, let me remind you that most of the vegetables necessary for a family of four can be grown on a plot of forty by sixty feet. I think we might see in this an economic potential of considerable importance, since we now appear to be facing the possibility of widespread famine. How much food could be grown in the dooryards of cities and suburbs? How much could be grown along the extravagant rights-of-way of the Interstate system? Or how much could be grown, by the intensive practices and economics of the small farm, on so-called marginal lands? Louis Bromfield liked to point out that the people of France survived crisis after crisis because they were a nation of gardeners, who in times of want turned with great skill to their own small plots of ground. And F. H. King, an agriculture professor who traveled extensively in the Orient in 1907, talked to a Chinese farmer who supported a family of twelve, "one donkey, one cow, . . . and two pigs on 2.5 acres of cultivated land" —and who did this, moreover, by agricultural methods that were sound enough organically to have maintained his land in prime fertility through several thousand years of such use. These are possibilities that are very readily apparent and attractive to minds that are prepared to think little. To Big Thinkers—the bureaucrats and businessmen of agriculture—they are quite simply invisible. But intensive, organic agriculture kept the farms of the Orient thriving for thousands of years, whereas extensive—which is to say, exploitive or extractive—agriculture has critically reduced the fertility of American farmlands in a few centuries or even a few decades.

A person who undertakes to grow a garden at home, by practices that will preserve rather than exploit the economy of the soil, has set his mind decisively against what is wrong with us. He is helping himself in a way that dignifies him, and that is rich in meaning and pleasure. But he is doing something else that is more important: he is making vital contact with the soil and the weather on which his life depends. He will no longer look upon rain as an impediment of traffic, or upon the sun as a holiday decoration. And his sense of man's dependence on the world will have grown precise enough, one would hope, to be politically clarifying and useful.

What I am saying is that if we apply our minds directly and competently to the needs of the earth, then we will have begun to make fundamental and very necessary changes in our minds. We will begin to understand and to mistrust *and to change* our wasteful economy, which markets not just the produce of the earth, but also the earth's ability to produce. We will see that beauty and utility are alike dependent upon the health of the world. But we will also see through the fads and the fashions of protest. We will see that war and oppression and pollution are not separate issues, but are aspects of the same issue. Amid the outcries for the liberation of this group or that, we will know that no person is free except in the freedom of other persons, and that man's only real freedom is to know and faithfully occupy his place—a much humbler place than we have been taught to think—in the order of creation. And we will know that of all issues in education the issue of relevance is the phoniest. If life were as predictable and small as the talkers of politics would have it, then relevance would be a consideration. But life is large and surprising and mysterious, and we don't know what we need to know. When I was a student I refused certain subjects because I thought they were irrelevant to the duties of a writer, and I have had to take them up, clumsily and late, to understand my duties as a man. What we need in education is not relevance, but abundance, variety, adventurousness, thoroughness. A student should suppose that he needs to learn everything he can, and he should suppose that he will need to know much more than he can learn.

But the change of mind I am talking about involves not just a change of knowledge, but also a change of attitude toward our essential ignorance, a change in our bearing in the face of mystery. The principle of ecology, if we will take it to heart, should keep us aware that our lives depend upon other lives and upon processes and energies in an interlocking system which, though we can destroy it completely, we can neither fully understand nor fully control. And our great dangerousness is that, locked in our selfish and myopic economics, we have been willing to change or destroy far beyond our power to understand. We are not humble enough or reverent enough.

Some time ago I heard a representative of a paper company refer to conservation as a "no-return investment." This man's thinking was exclusively oriented to the annual profit of his industry. Circumscribed by the demand that the profit be great, he simply could not be answerable to any other demand—not even to the obvious needs of his own children.

Consider, in contrast, the profound ecological intelligence of Black Elk, "a holy man of the Oglala Sioux," who in telling his story said that it was not his own life that was important to him, but what he had shared with all life: "It is the story of all life that is holy and it is good to tell, and of us two-leggeds sharing in it with the four-leggeds and the wings of the air and all green things. . . ." And of the great vision that came to him when he was a child he said: "I saw that the sacred hoop of my people was one of many hoops that made one circle, wide as daylight and as starlight, and in the center grew one mighty flowering tree to shelter all the children of one mother and father. And I saw that it was holy."

For Discussion and Review

1. Berry states that he would "rather go before government with two men who have a competent understanding of an issue, and who therefore *deserve* a hearing, than to go with two thousand who are vaguely dissatisfied." What assumption about lobbying underlies this statement? How valid do you consider it to be?
2. Why does Berry disparage Thinking Big and two of its results, plan-making and law-making? On what basis could you argue against his views?
3. Explain what Berry means when he says that "individualism is going around these days in uniform, handing out the party line on individualism." What is wrong with this form of individualism?
4. Are you more shocked by a statement in the newspaper of the fifty thousand highway deaths a year or by the fatality of a single friend? Relate your answer to Berry's thesis.

SOLUTION

But Who Will Pay the Piper and Will It Be in Time?

BY VICTOR COHN

We have finally set out to rise from the muck, to halt pollution and cleanse the world. Or have we? There are many reasons to conclude that we have not yet made a true start.

On February 10 [1970] to be sure, President Nixon called for a "total mobilization" against pollution and the most far-reaching environmental program yet proposed by any President. "Ecology," says California's Jesse Unruh, "has become the political substitute for the word 'mother.'" And Senator Edmund Muskie adds: "In the past we had to fight against all kinds of political pressure, public apathy and ignorance. Now the wind is blowing at our backs."

Hallelujah! Even Dr. Barry Commoner—outdone by no one as an ecological Jeremiah (with a high average for accuracy)—now states, "I think there's some hope. I think we may barely make it if we organize all our resources to support human needs."

So far, however, we have seen mainly the words. All the essential actions, though sincerely promised we will concede are still to come.

On March 11, 1964—remember?—President Lyndon B. Johnson pledged an equally resounding "unconditional war against poverty," to the same sort of hosannas. We have heard similar declarations of war against racial inequality, against unequal education, against urban squalor and against war itself. The typical pattern of the New American Crusade is words followed by ill-funded and inadequate programs

Victor Cohn is Science Editor for the *Washington Post* and the author of *1999 Our Hopeful Future*. He has been the recipient of many awards and honors in the field of journalism and writes a widely syndicated column.

Victor Cohn, "But Who Will Pay the Piper and Will It Be in Time?" *Smithsonian*, May 1970, pp. 15–22. Copyright Smithsonian National Associates, 1970. Reprinted by permission.

followed by disillusionment followed by apathy. What makes us think we can now avoid the same route?

True, we sent men to the moon, but that was technologically simple compared with assaulting pollution. This job demands not a nicely delimited, eight-year, $25-billion program, but a far more expensive, everlasting effort dictating profound changes in the lives of all of us.

The job must be accomplished by most of the same individuals and officials who have been doing or permitting the polluting. In 1965, for example, Congress enacted what seemed to be a strong and far-reaching joint federal-state water quality program. Today the nation's waters are even dirtier, and negotiations are still going on with many states over adequate goals.

Many industrialists, such as Henry Ford II, have impressively pledged themselves to the environment. But we kid ourselves if we think that industry as a whole—with "low-cost production" its lifeblood —will passively swallow expensive measures. Company after company is already scrutinizing the fine print and cutting the costs in the new enforcement bills now being written. The pressure on Congress for loopholes for this or that state's crucial industry, and crucial jobs will be huge.

"Ecology is the most perishable item to come along in years," says Dr. Harvey Wheeler of Santa Barbara's Center for the Study of Democratic Institutions. "We've got a program to invent a new name for ecology, so we can keep it alive after it's been talked to death."

All these are dark facts. There is also a bright one. People are complaining. What Harvard ecologist Frederick Smith calls "the wrath of the people" has at last exploded. Little Trenton, Maine, badly in need of new taxation and jobs, voted 144 to 77 to reject a new aluminum reduction plant and nuclear power station. A Houston TV station asked listeners to comment on the air on local pollution; it got 80,000 responses.

Why today? Perhaps it was the photographs of those pathetic oil-soaked birds at Santa Barbara that first woke up the country to the fact that the mess is everywhere. Passing south of Chicago, you have to roll up your car windows. Open an apartment window in downtown Washington, a non-industrial city, and you get a roomful of soot. "Just look around," says a University of Minnesota co-ed. "The air, the water, the roadsides—everything stinks." An Indiana girl says: "There are no pretty days in Terre Haute."

Indeed, the kids—newly incensed about the environment as they have long been incensed about the war—seem to have found a cause that unites campus longhairs and squares. . . . Ask them, "Why *now*?" and many complain of a "system" that, in permitting war, in oppressing blacks, in fouling the earth, always seems to them to put people last.

The politicians are listening. Governors and legislative leaders in virtually all the states have put environmental bills at or near the top of this year's priority list. . . .

So we're all in the battle. In the immortal words of Pogo, quoted about every other day on this newly popular subject: "We have met the enemy and they is us."

In all of the talk and the programs so far, however, there has been mightly little "us." Most of us piously say "they" must cut down on pollution, "they" must clean up their plants, "they" must build better cars. There is still deep failure in most quarters—including the state-houses and the nation's capital—to grapple with the fact that it will be costly for all of *us*, will bear down on *our* present liberties, force *us* to reduce our consumption of inevitably polluting luxuries like gasoline and electricity and force *us* to limit population, not just in distant India but in our own families.

We have no choice but to try. It is fashionable in some circles still to scoff at those who say we may have "only 15 or 30 or x" more years before mankind may be irretrievably doomed. Yet this globe has witnessed the extinction of many species; there is no reason why man should be magically exempt.

Ecologists are worried about the future of the oceanic phytoplankton, which produce some 70 percent of our oxygen. They are worried about mass deaths in cities (Los Angeles public schools forbid children to exercise on some days lest they inhale too much smog).

MELTING ICECAPS OR A NEW ICE AGE?

Some oceanographers say that at present rates of pollution—by sewage sludge, by oil-drilling and spills, by man's chemicals—the continental shelves of all major oceans will be so fouled that oceanic productivity "will be essentially over" in perhaps as few as 25 years. Atmospheric scientists are increasingly worried about rising levels of atmospheric carbon dioxide, put there by proliferating, fuel-burning man. The result is a "greenhouse effect" that may make the planet warm up—melting icecaps and flooding coastal cities—*or* may reflect away sunlight, causing a new ice age. Just what will happen no one in fact knows, but one scientist feels sure there will be "dramatic effects" —reduced snowfalls perhaps, reduced river flows, melted glaciers— "within 50 years" if world population and fossil fuel burning keep increasing.

Barry Commoner (just as a "wild estimate," he admits) thinks we may have only until the end of the century—the point when today's world population of 3.5 billion may reach 7 billion—to halt further population growth and pollution or so disturb the phytoplankton or some other part of the ecosystem "that we will have had it." Some scientists think this is extreme. But the world's population will double every 35 years after the year 2000, if it continues at the present rate. No one thinks the planet can survive this for long.

The only question then is: What do we do? Where do we start?

The answer is fairly simple and, in a political world, political. We have to start by enacting the kind of programs Mr. Nixon asked, and, if they are not enough, be prepared to build and expand on them—instead of quickly abandoning them as "failures" as is our wont (example: the war on poverty).

We need to enact at least the nationwide air and water standards which the President asked, and at least his proposed penalties, which are up to $10,000 a day for industrial or civic polluters. But even $10,000 a day (or more than $300,000 a month) may not deter some major polluters (it's less than paying eight percent interest on a $45 million loan for new equipment). This means other penalties will be required, including jail sentences, if needed, for defying court orders. Tough enforcement, not just new laws, will be the real test of federal purpose. For enforcement, not law, has always been anti-pollution's main weakness. When a federal prosecutor recently cited an 1899 law in moving against Midwest water polluters, Ralph Nader asked: "Why wasn't it enforced for 71 years?"

HOW "ENFORCEMENT" IS WORKING TODAY

New York law said that 3,420 New York City apartment-house incinerators had to be upgraded or shut down by December 1968; as of January 1970, more than 1,900 (500 of them operated by the New York City Housing Authority itself) were still burning. As of October [1969], owners of 5,910 more were required to comply; as of January 1, 4,700 were operating. In Philadelphia last December, the Municipal Court disposed of a set of alleged air pollution violators as follows: "Philadelphia Electric Co., fined $6 (court costs); General Smelting Co., discharged; Celotex Corp., $6; National Steel Drum Co., $300 (the maximum fine)" etc. "The first three," noted the *Philadelphia Inquirer*, "are among the 15 major sources of air pollution identified by the city last year."

In such situations, it seems plain, a higher government must be prepared to move in on laggards. Similarly, far stronger regional authorities are needed—to revive, say, a Lake Erie, bordered by four states and Canada and now threatened with new gas and oil drilling. Or to arbitrate the mounting problem of municipal solid waste disposal. Every city is running out of dumping space and looking elsewhere. Who is to coordinate all the elsewheres, and prevent some small town from permitting the filling-in of a precious wetland just for some easy revenue?

Often, again, federal coordination and control will be the only possible "regional" authority. But federal policy itself has been a crazy quilt. The Interior Department tries to acquire wetlands and waterfowl areas for conservation purposes; the Department of Agriculture subsidizes drainage projects to dry them up. Health, Education and Welfare condemns foods high in pesticide residues and recommends pesticide curbs; Agriculture resists wholesale bans on pesticides.

We may need a whole set of new tax policies at all levels to assist the process to penalize polluters, for example, by assessing them for pollution; to encourage land preservation rather than encouraging endless development. Each year the United States is paving over one million acres of oxygen-creating vegetation. "We cannot afford this" just in terms of fresh oxygen to breathe, warns Dr. LaMont C. Cole of Cornell.

"Pollution taxes" or not, cleaning up the environment will take money. We need to be prepared to pay a heavy price, though the "savings," in a cleaner, more livable planet, will be priceless.

The immediate price? The United States, in federal, state, local and industrial funds, has been spending about one percent of the Gross National Product, or about $10 billion a year, on pollution control. (Half is consumed just by municipal waste collection.) The federal share in fiscal 1969 was under $1 billion. The President has mainly proposed adding $4 billion over four years, to supplement the communities' $6 billion, a total of $10 billion worth of water-treatment plants. Senator Muskie would have the government instead obligate $12.5 billion over this period, with states and localities matching it for a $25-billion total. The Federal Water Pollution Control Administration has estimated that bringing lakes and streams to federal standards by 1973 would truly cost from $26 to $29 billion.

Economists of the Organization for Economic Cooperation and Development think it would take a steady annual outlay of two percent of GNP (just under $20 billion in the United States) for an industrial nation *merely* to keep environmental deterioration gradual; that it would take a regular four percent to hold the line; and that real cleanup and prevention would cost "three or four times as much," or a U.S. minimum of $120 billion a year.

All these are guesses. There is undoubtedly much that can be done cheaply. We can probably develop lead-free gasoline for an added four cents a gallon at most; we can probably drive something close to pollution-free automobiles for an extra $300 to $500 apiece. One estimate says a $700-million annual national charge for "drastic" control of industrial and power-plant pollution would add "a mere 20 to 30 cents" to most users' monthly electricity bills. But Dr. S. Fred Singer, deputy assistant secretary of the Interior for scientific programs, is not as optimistic. As U.S. population rises, he believes, anti-pollution costs will rise even faster. The American taxpayer, he fears, will soon refuse to pay them, preferring pollution.

This means that we may soon have to decide a question far more basic. If we would really keep a clean planet, we first must decide what kind of society we want.

We can have anti-pollution auto engines, but they will still have to run on some kind of energy, which will require mining or offshore oil drilling or electric plants. Can we really afford to let individuals have cars at all? Or all the cars they can buy?

WE MAY HAVE TO GO BACK TO BEING HOT IN THE SUMMER

We can build lower-pollution electric power plants at acceptable cost, very probably, for a while. But even they will cause some pollution and require smokestacks that tower over landscapes and peaceful rivers. U.S. power needs are now doubling every ten years, far faster than the population. Can we really let everyone consume all the electricity he wants—for electric typewriters, electric pencil sharpeners, electric can openers, hair driers, knife shapeners, shoe polishers? Do we really need endless miles of neon signs, scarring the roadsides and confusing drivers as well as eating up scarce energy? Do we really need air conditioning on days in the pleasant '70s, just because big buildings are now being erected with sealed windows (to keep out the pollution that this overuse of energy causes)?

Can we indeed ecologically afford endless economic growth? The voracious United States, with 5.7 percent of the world's people, already consumes 40 percent of its resource production and spews out 50 percent of its industrial pollution. Isn't there some point where the factories have to stop growing, where we say, "This is the richest living, the largest production of goods we can ecologically tolerate"?

Harvey Wheeler thinks the United States may reach the point in just ten years when "the present rate is absolutely disastrous and economic growth may have to be abandoned altogether." According to Dr. William Pollard, director of the Oak Ridge Associated Universities, we must face the fact that the Industrial Revolution's "joyride" is almost over.

There are some signs that some people are ready. Many of the kids are deriding our "junk culture" and saying they are ready to settle for less. Astonishing all observers (and oil company lobbyists), the Maine legislature recently overwhelmingly voted statewide industrial zoning and tough new bills to control industrial development. It required the oil industry, for example, to pay unlimited liability for oil spills, plus a half-cent environmental levy on every barrel of oil moved in or out of the state. It did this despite intense industry interest in building refineries on the Maine coast, interest that would have been greeted with open arms and easy rules a few years ago.

But the issue of economic growth versus environmental quality will not go away so easily. Economist Walter Heller believes that prosperity without economic growth is unthinkable, and that continued growth will in fact be mandatory if we are to pay for pollution control.

Black militants are calling environmental concern a "cop-out" and "white middle-class toy," designed to steal attention from poverty. *Newsweek* quotes a black steelworker who is rearing his family in the dubious air of Gary, Indiana: "It's the bread, man. Hell, I'm getting $5.50 an hour."

The only possible answer here is a larger definition of "environment." Harvard's Dr. Smith says: "Environmental quality and human welfare are not two independent evaluations," but "two views of the same system. . . . It is not possible for one to remain good while the other is bad. . . . Under this broad definition of environment all of the ills of man emerge as environmental problems."

So we need only reform the world, a task that has eluded man for all his years.

We very badly need knowledge. Knowledge is lacking today to answer many of the most basic questions about the environment.

A study board of the National Academy of Sciences in January [1970] accordingly recommended three steps: (1) a day-to-day national program to monitor pollution; (2) creation of a National Index of Environmental Quality to measure the purity of air and water, the uses of land and the state of various animal species; (3) establishment of a National Laboratory for the Environmental Sciences.

We need answers to many questions. The $10 billion in sewage plants the President wants to finance will put clean-looking effluent into the rivers all right, but the effluent will be rich in both phosphorus and nitrogen compounds that promote plant growth and eutrophication—or death—for rivers and lakes.

We desperately need better ways of waste disposal than burning and dumping, which either create new smog or fill in our last wetlands or create new dead zones at sea. The only possible answer is recycling: reusing everything; building in new charges or subsidies to make this profitable; putting every product in a reusable or reclaimable container. But today there are a thousand competing and often half-baked recycling ideas. These need research and development programs on a scale not yet even considered—perhaps under something like a reconverted NASA with a new national goal: to put man on a clean earth in this decade.

THE PERILS OF USING HAND-PICKED CONSULTANTS

To understand all we are doing and will yet do to the environment, we need advance examination of our massive assaults on the limited earth. A case in point: In 1969 the Atomic Energy Commission said a "safety review" foresaw no substantial risks in hugely expanded underground nuclear testing, even near the earthquake-prone West Coast and in the unstable Aleutians. Dr. Kenneth Pitzer, president of Stanford University and former A.E.C. research director, demurred. He did not disagree with the A.E.C. finding, but he urged study of such an important matter—where mistake means disaster—by "an impartial judge and jury" of independent experts outside the A.E.C.

We should follow the same practice, Dr. Pitzer argued, in many decisions that affect earthly ecology—instead of making them in closed circles, in unpublicized meetings, by government officials and closely-linked, often hand-picked consultants.

We face many ecological decisions today:

In transportation, for example. We have poured billions into highway development but almost nothing into developing other ground transport. Travelers today may spend one hour flying from Washington to New York, then five hours circling in the air, waiting on the ground and finally traveling by various means a distance of 30 miles. How long must we wait for an ecologically sane transport system?

Energy production is another such area. Citizens of Minnesota, Maryland, Maine, New York, New Jersey and elsewhere are now demonstrating and making strict rules against the radioactivity of nuclear power plants. At the same time, citizens of California are legislating against dirty fossil power, and complaining of tardy development there of cleaner-seeming nuclear power. Which will really do the least harm to a particular environment? Can't someone say?

Then there is our use of precious land. To preserve open land, we may have to make the federal government its major controller. . . . We also need planned towns instead of uncontrolled sprawl—including experimental cities, some scientists believe, to test new ways of closed system sewage control and water reuse. Who is now planning these?

All such decisions and more require "technology assessment," but do not now get it, though we put up whole "new cities" in haphazard fashion every year. However we do it, if we ever do it—man does not always do the rational thing—it will still not give us perfect answers, only the familiar imperfect alternatives, but we will have to get used to that.

For we must see now that there are no perfect solutions to most of our technological problems. Science is a wondrous servant, but it cannot do everything. We will never again see the earthly environment of 1900 or even 1950.

We will not even maintain the environment of 1970, however, unless we face the most basic question of all—the one we all tend to face last, if ever. How many children can we allow future parents to have? "Allow" means not only persuasion and social and economic engineering, but also harsher measures like severe tax laws, if necessary.

A CRUSADE LAUNCHED WITH EARRINGS

In June [1969] a dignified 20-year-old named Miss Stephanie Mills (quoting *The New York Times*) "jarred the Mills College commencement at Oakland, California, by announcing, as valedictorian, that she did not intend to bring any children into this muddled world." Miss Mills appeared at Stanford in November to address students meeting to form an environmental federation. Having become a worker for Planned Parenthood, she now wore a conspicuous set of curlicue-shaped plastic earrings: intrauterine contraceptives. Fine. For her. Yet most of us would still say, IUDs yes, childlessness no. Otherwise we concede that man's extinction has already begun.

What we may have to accept, many scientists believe, is zero population growth by about the year 2000, when world population, it seems, will inevitably be doubled no matter what we start doing now. What we will have to accept *now* to affect population growth later, many demographers think, is the family of two as a universal limit. Will establishing zero population growth and the two-child family require more coercion than social measures or taxes? We can only hope not, while saying deep inside, "Probably—some unfine day."

Our only alternative, in the phrase of Margaret Mead, would be "a new planetary ethic," one that would say: we *cannot* overpopulate, we *cannot* overconsume, we *cannot* pollute.

It is certain that we are not all going to start to wear IUD earrings, to say "We cop out." It is equally certain that individual morality, not just the law, is required to curb the deadly litter that each of us generates. It is equally certain that we must begin to move far past the President's . . . message if we would leave our children an earth.

For Discussion and Review

1. Compare Cohn's point of view to that of Berry. In what respect do they disagree about Thinking Big?
2. Cohn warns against our following a familiar pattern that has occurred in crusades on other social ills. Describe this pattern, using recent examples, and discuss the reasons for it.
3. Cohn feels that there must be federal instead of state or local pollution policies. Explain why you agree or disagree with him. What difficulties would be involved if pollution policies were formulated entirely by the federal government or entirely at the local level?
4. Why do you think Cohn states that the population question is the "one we all tend to face last, if ever"?

SOLUTION

Introduction to Ecotactics

BY RALPH NADER

For centuries, man's efforts to control nature brought increasing security from trauma and disease. Cultures grew rapidly by harnessing the forces of nature to work and produce for proliferating populations. But in recent decades, the imbalanced application of man's energies to the land, water and air has abused these resources to a point where nature is turning on its abusers. The natural conditions of human health and safety are being subjected to complex and savage assaults. Yet these assaults are no longer primarily aesthetic and economic deprivations. They are now threatening the physiological integrity of our citizens. They are exacting their insidious toll daily. During the past decade, this country has begun to show that it can destroy itself inadvertently from within. Surely, this capability must be something new in the history of man.

In taking the initiative against those whose myopia, venality and indifference produce pollution, the first step is to equate the phenomena to our basic value system. Pollution is violence and environmental pollution is environmental violence. It is a violence that has different impacts, styles and time factors than the more primitive kind

Ralph Nader, a lawyer, has taught at the University of Hartford and at Princeton. Author of *Unsafe at Any Speed* and innumerable articles, he is best known as a consumer advocate, whose task-force groups have written such reports as *Water Wasteland* and *Vanishing Air*.
Ralph Nader, "Introduction to Ecotactics," in *Ecotactics*, a Sierra Club Handbook (New York: Pocket Books, 1970), pp. 13–22. Copyright © 1970 by the Sierra Club. Reprinted by permission of Pocket Books, a division of Simon & Schuster, Inc.

of violence such as crime in the streets. Yet in the size of the population exposed and the seriousness of the harm done, environmental violence far exceeds that of street crime.

Why then is there so much more official and citizen concern over crime in the streets? Some of the reasons are obvious. Primitive crime provokes sensory perceptions of a raw, instinctual nature; environmental crime generates a silent form of violence most often unfelt, unseen and unheard. Environmental crime is often accompanied by the production of economic and governmental benefits: consequently the costs are played down, especially since people other than the polluters are bearing them. The slogan, "that's the price of progress," is more than superficially ingrained in people continually confronted by industry arguments that any pollution crackdown will mean loss of jobs. Another reason is that power and polluters have always been closely associated. The corporate drive to reduce corporate costs and invest only in machinery and systems that enhance sales and profits is calculated to inflict as social costs on the public the contaminants of corporate activities. The same is true for the lack of attention by producers to the post-production fallout of their products as they interact, run off and become waste. Pesticides, nitrogen fertilizer and disposable containers are examples of such fallout.

Governmental activity in sewage and solid waste disposal and in defense research has also burgeoned environmental violence. Deep-well disposal of chemical wastes by the U.S. Army near Denver led to earth tremors and small earthquakes as well as to contamination of the subsoil. The Navy dumps tons of raw sewage into offshore waters, and its facilities, such as the notorious Fire Fighting School in San Diego, throw off pollutants into the air. Vessels carrying herbicides to Viet Nam and other areas of the world could possibly provoke one of history's greatest catastrophes: Should one ship sink and should the drums containing the chemicals be ruptured, marine organisms for miles around would be destroyed, thus reducing the oxygen supply available to mankind. The transfer of these herbicides through food to humans is another specter, given the fantastic geometric progress of the concentration of these chemicals from plankton on up the food-chain to man himself. Municipal waste disposal practices are, for many towns and cities, primitive; and where waste is treated, effluents still upset the ecology of lakes, streams and bays.

To deal with a system of oppression and suppression, which characterizes the environmental violence in this country, the first priority is to deprive the polluters of their unfounded legitimacy. Too often they assume a conservative, patriotic posture when in reality they are radical destroyers of a nation's resources and the most fundamental rights of people. Their power to block or manipulate existing laws permits them, as perpetrators, to keep the burden of proof on the victims. In a country whose people have always valued the "open book," corporate and government polluters crave secrecy and deny citizens access to the records of that which is harming their health and safety.

State and federal agencies keep undisclosed data on how much different companies pollute. Thus has industrial lethality been made a trade secret by a government that presumes to be democratic. Corporate executives—as in the auto companies—speak out against violence in the streets and are not brought to account for their responsibility in producing a scale of violence that utterly dwarfs street crime. Motor vehicles contribute at least 60 percent of the nation's air pollution by tonnage, with one company—General Motors—contributing 35 percent of the pollution tonnage. Many companies respond to critics by saying that they conform with legal pollution control standards. While this claim is often untrue—again as in the case of the domestic auto companies that are in widespread violation of vehicle pollution standards —the point must be made continually in rebuttal that the industries wrote much of the laws, stripped them of effective sanctions, starved their projected budgets and daily surrounded their administrators with well-funded lobbyists. The same industry spokesmen who assert the value of freedom of choice by consumers fail to recognize the massive, forced consumption inflicted on consumers and their progeny by industrial contaminants.

Until citizens begin to focus on this curious relationship between our most traditional values and their destruction by the polluters, moral indignation and pressures for change at the grass roots will not be effective. Effective action demands that full responsibility be imposed on polluters in the most durable, least costly and administratively feasible manner. The social costs of pollution must be cycled back to the polluter so that they are prevented at the earliest stage of the production or processing sequence. Achievement of this objective —whether dealing with automobiles, chemical plants or municipal waste disposal systems—requires communicating to the public and to pertinent authorities the known or knowable technological remedies. Moral imperatives to act become much more insistent with greater technical capability to do the job. Too many of our citizens have little or no understanding of the relative ease with which industry has or can obtain the technical solutions. As a result, too often the popular impression—encouraged by industry advertisements—is that industry is working at the limits of technology in controlling its pollution. This, of course, is nonsense. Furthermore, an action strategy must embrace the most meticulous understanding of the corporate structure—its points of access, its points of maximum responsiveness, its specific motivational sources and its constituencies.

General Motors is considered a producer of automobiles. It is time to view that company (and others like it) not only in the light of its impact on the economy but of its impact on urban and rural land use through its infernal internal combustion engines, on our solid waste disposal problem through its lack of attention to the problem of junked cars, on a huge diversion of public resources through the inefficiency of vehicle operation and designed-in repair and replacement costs, on water through its polluting plants, on safety of passengers through unsafe design and on a more rational, clean transportation system through its historic opposition to the development of mass transit. As a corporate state with annual revenues exceeding that of any foreign government except the Soviet Union, GM's average hourly gross around the clock of $2.4 million makes it a force of considerable substance.

Very little scholarly or action-oriented attention has been paid to such corporations, 200 of which control over two-thirds of the manufacturing assets of the country. This state of affairs is due to the curtain of secrecy surrounding corporate behavior and the great faith placed by citizens on the efficacy of governmental regulations. Corporations represent the most generic power system in the country. As such, layering their transgressions with governmental controls without treating the underlying system of corporate power simply leads, as it has done since the establishment of the Interstate Commerce Commission in 1887, to the take-over of the regulators by the regulatees. This is not to say that government agencies offer little potential for disciplining corporate polluters. It is only to emphasize that the restrictive hands of industry power must be lifted before these regulatory agencies can be returned to the people. But now there are indications that a business-oriented Administration will further develop a system of subsidizing the control of corporate pollution through liberal tax provisions, permissive attitudes toward unjustified price increases, and more direct payments. Such techniques have proved to be highly wasteful and inefficient and require the closest scrutiny both as policy and in operation.

Citizens' strategies for effecting corporate responsibility are concededly primitive. This is an area for great pioneering imagination and insight on the part of citizens willing to view the corporation not as a monolith but as a composition of different groups inside and attached to it. A partial list of these groups illustrates the broad opportunities for finding access and bringing pressure for change. The list includes unions, employees, institutional and individual shareholders, creditors, pensioneers, suppliers, customers, dealers, law firms, trade associations, professional societies, state and federal regulatory agencies, and state attorney generals. To be sure, many of these groups or individuals are presently unencouraging prospects for helping one tame the corporate tiger. But recent years have shown how rapidly matters can change when committeed youth are at large with unyielding stamina.

Youth must develop an investigative approach to the problems of pollution. It is one of the most basic prerequisites. Not only must there be a close analysis of corporate statements, and periodicals, annual reports, patents, correspondence, court records, regulations, technical papers, Congressional hearings and agency reports and transcripts, but there must be a search for the dissenting company engineer, the conscience-stricken house lawyer, the concerned retiree or ex-employee, the knowledgeable worker and the fact-laden supplier of the industry or company under study. They are there somewhere. They must be located.

Top corporate executives crave anonymity and almost uniformly decline to appear at universities and colleges to speak or exchange thoughts with students. This reticence is a functional one from their point of view. It perpetuates the secrecy, the detachment and the tight-knit circle that is corporate America. It hides the quantity and quality of the decisions which pollute the environment. To widen the arena of discourse and to expose these top, often insulated, executives to the urgencies of the times, a consistent effort to bring them on campus should be undertaken.

This quest should fit in with the formal educational curricula. The problems of environmental pollution and their origins are challenges to almost every discipline of the university, from physical science to the humanities. The curricula must be made to respond to our need for knowledge about the ecosystem. Formal course work, independent and summer work can involve empirical research, even the development of new environmental strategies. Formal education—to have a lasting legacy for the student—should thus strive to combine the development *in tandem* of technical skills and a humane value system. Action for ecological integrity has to be viewed as a process of endless discovery. To map the terrain, one must cover the terrain. There is no manual ready to guide, only a world to discover.

For Discussion and Review

1. Why does Nader think that the public is more concerned about crime in the streets than about the wholesale pollution of our environment? Discuss whether or not you agree with his reasoning.
2. Why does Nader believe that a complete understanding of corporate structure is necessary before anti-pollution measures can be effective?
3. Since Nader advocates measures that will lead to group action, do you think he is in total disagreement with Berry as to how environmental problems can best be solved? Why or why not?

Recommended Readings

George Borgstrom, *The Hungry Planet* (New York: The Macmillan Company, 1965).

George Borgstrom, *Too Many* (New York: The Macmillan Company, 1969).

Barry Commoner, *Science and Survival* (New York: The Viking Press, Inc., 1966).

J. Y. Costeau, *The Living Sea* (New York: Harper & Row, 1963).

Garrett De Bell, ed., *The Environmental Handbook* (New York: Ballantine Books, Inc., 1970).

Rene Dubos, *So Human an Animal* (New York: Charles Scribner's Sons, 1970).

Paul R. Ehrlich, *The Population Bomb* (New York: Ballantine Books, Inc., 1968).

Paul R. Ehrlich and Anne H. Ehrlich, *Population, Resources, Environment: Issues in Human Ecology* (San Francisco: W. H. Freeman and Co., 1970).

Richard Fagley, *Population Explosion and Christian Responsibility* (New York: Oxford University Press, 1960).

Peter Farb, *Face of North America* (New York: Harper & Row, 1968).

James Fisher et al., *Wildlife in Danger* (The Viking Press, Inc., 1968).

Ronald Freedman, *Population: The Vital Revolution* (Garden City, N.Y.: Doubleday & Company, Inc., 1964).

Frank Graham, Jr., *Man's Dominion: A History of Conservation in America* (New York: M. Evans & Co., Inc., 1971).

Frank Graham, *Since Silent Spring* (Boston: Houghton Mifflin Company, 1970).

Michael Hamilton, ed., *This Little Planet* (New York: Charles Scribner's Sons, 1970).

Garrett Hardin, ed., *Population, Evolution, and Birth Control: A Collage of Controversial Ideas,* 2nd ed. (San Francisco: W. H. Freeman and Co., 1969).

David M. Heer, ed., *Readings on Population* (Englewood Cliffs, N.J.: Prentice-Hall, Inc., 1968).

Harold Helfrich, Jr., ed., *Environmental Crisis: Man's Struggle to Live with Himself* (New Haven, Conn.: Yale University Press, 1970).

Theodora Kroeber, *Ishi: The Last of His Tribe* (Berkeley: Parnassus Press, 1964).

Joseph Wood Krutch, *The Best Nature Writing of Joseph Wood Krutch* (New York: William Morrow & Co., Inc., 1970).

Joseph Wood Krutch, *The Great Chain of Life* (Boston: Houghton Mifflin Company, 1957).

Aldo Leopold, *A Sand County Almanac* (New York: Ballantine Books, Inc., 1970); originally published in 1949.

Gene Marine, *America the Raped* (New York: Simon & Schuster, Inc., 1969).

George P. Marsh, *Man and Nature* (Cambridge, Mass.: Harvard University Press, 1965).

Wesley Marx, *The Frail Ocean* (New York: Coward, McCann & Geohegan, Inc., 1967).

Maxine McCloskey and Joseph P. Gilligan, eds., *Wilderness and the Quality of Life* (San Francisco: Sierra Club Books, 1969).

Desmond Morris, *The Naked Ape* (New York: Dell Publishing Co., Inc., 1969).

Charles B. Nam, ed., *Population and Society: A Textbook of Selected Readings* (Boston: Houghton Mifflin Company, 1968).

Roderick Nash, *Wilderness and the American Mind* (New Haven, Conn.: Yale University Press, 1967).

Max Nicholson, *The Environmental Revolution* (New York: McGraw-Hill Book Company, 1970).

Robert Osborn, *Mankind May Never Make It!* (Greenwich, Conn.: New York Graphic Society, Ltd., 1968).

William and Paul Paddock, *Famine—1975* (Boston: Little, Brown and Company, 1967).

William Petersen, *Population,* 2nd ed. (New York: The Macmillan Company, 1969).

Roger Revelle and Hans H. Landsberg, eds., *America's Changing Environment* (Boston: Beacon Press, 1970).

James Ridgeway, *The Politics of Pollution* (New York: E. P. Dutton & Co., Inc., 1970).

Robert and Leona Rienow, *Moment in the Sun* (New York: Ballantine Books, Inc., 1967).

Berton Roueche, *What's Left: Reports on a Diminishing America* (Boston: Little, Brown and Company, 1969).

John and Mildred Teal, *Life and Death of the Salt Marsh* (Boston: The Atlantic Monthly Press, 1971).

Henry David Thoreau, *Walden* (New York: Dodd, Mead & Co., 1955); originally published in 1854.

Stewart Udall, *1976: Agenda for Tomorrow* (New York: Harcourt Brace Jovanovich, Inc., 1968).

Stewart Udall, *The Quiet Crisis* (New York: Holt, Rinehart & Winston, Inc., 1963).

Charles Zorhurst, *The Conservation Fraud* (New York: Cowles Book Co., Inc., 1969).